1/ 50p

48

# Carrying On—

## After
## The First Hundred Thousand

# Carrying On—

## After
# The First Hundred Thousand

BY

## IAN HAY

William Blackwood and Sons
Edinburgh and London
1917

# AUTHOR'S NOTE.

*The First Hundred Thousand* closed with the Battle of Loos. The present narrative follows certain friends of ours from the scene of that costly but valuable experience, through a winter campaign in the neighbourhood of Ypres and Ploegsteert, to profitable participation in the Battle of the Somme.

Much has happened since then. The initiative has passed once and for all into our hands; so has the command of the air. Russia has been reborn, and like most healthy infants, is passing through an uproarious period of teething trouble; but America has stepped in, and promises to do more than redress the balance. All along the Western Front we have begun to move forward, without haste or flurry, but in

such wise that during the past twelve
months no position, once fairly captured
and consolidated, has ever been regained
by the enemy. To-day you can stand upon
certain recently-won eminences—Wytschaete
Ridge, Messines Ridge, Vimy Ridge, and
Monchy — looking down into the enemy's
lines, and looking forward to the territory
which yet remains to be restored to France.

You can also look back—not merely from
these ridges, but from certain moral ridges
as well—over the ground which has been
successfully traversed, and you can marvel
for the hundredth time, not that the thing
was well or badly done, but that it was
ever done at all.

But while this narrative was being written
none of these things had happened. We
were still struggling uphill, with inadequate
resources. So, since the incidents of the
story were set down, in the main, as they
occurred and when they occurred, the reader
will find very little perspective, a great deal
of the mood of the moment, and none at
all of that profound wisdom which comes
after the event. For the latter he must
look home—to the lower walks of journal-

ism and the back benches of the House of Commons.

It is not proposed to carry this story to a third volume. The First Hundred Thousand, as such, are no more. Like the 'Old Contemptibles,' they are now merged in a greater and more victorious army—in an armed nation, in fact. And, as Sergeant Mucklewame once observed to me, "There's no' that mony of us left now, onyways." So with all reverence — remembering how, when they were needed most, these men did not pause to reason why or count the cost, but came at once—we bid them good-bye.

# CONTENTS.

# Carrying On—

## After The First Hundred Thousand.

———•———

### CHAPTER ONE.

#### WINTER QUARTERS.

IT is the late autumn of 1915, and we
are getting into our stride again. Two
months ago we trudged into Bethune, gaunt,
dirty, soaked to the skin, and reduced to a
comparative handful. None of us had had
his clothes off for a week. Our ankle-
puttees had long dropped to pieces, and our
hose-tops, having worked under the soles of
our boots, had been cut away and discarded.
The result was a bare and mud-splashed ex-
panse of leg from boot to kilt, except in the
case of the enterprising few who had devised

artistic spat-puttees out of an old sandbag. Our headgear consisted in a few cases of the regulation Balmoral bonnet, usually minus "toorie" and badge; in a few more, of the battered remains of a gas helmet; and in the great majority, of a woollen cap - comforter. We were bearded like that incomparable fighter, the *poilu*, and we were separated by an abyss of years, so our stomachs told us, from our last square meal.

But we were wonderfully placid about it all. Our regimental pipers, who had come out to play us in, were making what the Psalmist calls "a joyful noise" in front; and behind us lay the recollection of a battle, still raging, in which we had struck the first blow, and borne our full share for three days and nights. Moreover, our particular blow had bitten deeper into the enemy's line than any other blow in the neighbourhood. And, most blessed thought of all, everything was over, and we were going back to rest. For the moment, the memory of the sights we had seen, and the tax we had levied upon our bodies and souls, together with the picture of the countless sturdy lads whom we had left lying beneath the sinister shade of Fosse

Eight, were beneficently obscured by the prospect of food, sleep, and comparative cleanliness.

After restoring ourselves to our personal comforts, we should doubtless go somewhere to refit. Drafts were already waiting at the Base to fill up the great gaps in our ranks. Our companies having been brought up to strength, a spate of promotions would follow. We had no Colonel, and only one Company Commander. Subalterns—what was left of them—would come by their own. N.C.O.'s, again, would have to be created by the dozen. While all this was going on, and the old names were being weeded out of the muster-roll to make way for the new, the Quartermaster would be drawing fresh equipment—packs, mess-tins, water-bottles, and the hundred oddments which always go astray in times of stress. There would be a good deal of dialogue of this sort—

"Private M'Sumph, I see you are down for a new pack. Where is your old one?"

"Blawn off ma back, sirr!"

"Where are your puttees?"

"Blawn off ma feet, sirr!"

"Where is your iron ration?"

"Blawn oot o' ma pooch, sirr!"

" Where is your head ? "

" Blawn—— I beg your pardon, sirr ! "—
followed by generous reissues all round.

After a month or so our beloved regiment,
once more at full strength, with traditions
and morale annealed by the fires of experience, would take its rightful place in the
forefront of " K (1)."

Such was the immediate future, as it presented itself to the wearied but optimistic
brain of Lieutenant Bobby Little. He communicated his theories to Captain Wagstaffe.

" I wonder ! " replied that experienced
officer.

## II.

The chief penalty of doing a job of work
well is that you are promptly put on to another. This is supposed to be a compliment.

The authorities allowed us exactly two days'
rest, and then packed us off by train, with
the new draft, to a particularly hot sector of
the trench line in Belgium—there to carry on
with the operation known in nautical circles
as " executing repairs while under steam."

Well, we have been in Belgium for two

months now, and, as already stated, are getting into our stride again.

There are new faces everywhere, and some of the old faces are not quite the same. They are finer-drawn; one is conscious of less chubbiness all round. War is a great maturing agent. There is, moreover, an air of seasoned authority abroad. Many who were second-lieutenants or lance-corporals three months ago are now commanding companies and platoons. Bobby Little is in command of "A" Company: if he can cling to this precarious eminence for thirty days—that is, if no one is sent out to supersede him—he becomes an "automatic" captain, aged twenty! Major Kemp commands the battalion; Wagstaffe is his senior major. Ayling has departed from our midst, and rumour says that he is leading a sort of Pooh Bah existence at Brigade Headquarters.

There are sad gaps among our old friends of the rank and file. Ogg and Hogg, M'Slattery and M'Ostrich, have gone to the happy hunting-grounds. Private Dunshie, the General Specialist (who, you may remember, found his true vocation, after many days, as battalion chiropodist), is reported "missing."

B

But his comrades are positive that no harm has befallen him. Long experience has convinced them that in the art of landing on his feet their departed friend has no equal.

"I doot he'll be a prisoner," suggests the faithful Mucklewame to the Transport Sergeant.

"Aye," assents the Transport Sergeant bitterly; "he'll be a prisoner. No doot he'll try to pass himself off as an officer, for to get better quarters!"

(The Transport Sergeant, in whose memory certain enormities of Dunshie had rankled ever since that versatile individual had abandoned the veterinary profession (owing to the most excusable intervention of a pack-mule's off hind-leg), was not far out in his surmise, as subsequent history may some day reveal. But the telling of that story is still a long way off.)

Company Sergeant - Major Pumpherston is now Sergeant - Major of the Battalion. Mucklewame is a corporal in his old company. Private Tosh was "offered a stripe" too, but declined, because the invitation did not include Private Cosh, who, owing to a regrettable lapse not unconnected with the rum ration, had been omitted from the Honours' List. Consequently these two grim veterans remain undecorated, but they are objects of great veneration among the recently joined for all that.

So you see us once more in harness, falling into the collar with energy, if not fervour. We no longer regard War with the least enthusiasm : we have seen It, face to face. Our sole purpose now is to screw our sturdy followers up to the requisite pitch of efficiency, and keep them remorsely at that standard until the dawn of triumphant and abiding peace.

We have one thing upon our side—youth.

"Most of our regular senior officers are gone, sir," remarked Colonel Kemp one day to the Brigadier—"dead, or wounded, or promoted to other commands ; and I have something like twenty new subalterns. When you subtract a centenarian like myself, the average age of our Battalion Mess, including Company Commanders, works out at something under twenty-three. But I am not exchanging any of them, thanks!"

### III.

Trench-life in Belgium is an entirely different proposition from trench-life in France. The undulating country in which we now find ourselves offers an infinite choice of unpleasant surroundings.

Down south, Vermelles way, the trenches stretch in a comparatively straight line for miles, facing one another squarely, and giving little opportunity for tactical enterprise. The infantry blaze and sputter at one another in front; the guns roar behind; and that is all there is to be said about it. But here, the line follows the curve of each little hill. At one place you are in a salient, in a trench which runs round the face of a bulging "knowe"—a tempting target for shells of every kind. A few hundred yards farther north, or south, the ground is much lower, and the trench line runs back into a re-entrant, seeking for a position which shall not be commanded from higher ground in front.

The line is pierced at intervals by railway cuttings, which have to be barricaded, and canals, which require special defences. Almost

every spot in either line is overlooked by some
adjacent ridge, or enfiladed from some adjacent
trench. It is disconcerting for a methodical
young officer, after cautiously scrutinising the
trench upon his front through a periscope, to
find that the entire performance has been
visible (and his entire person exposed) to the
view of a Boche trench situated on a hill-slope
upon his immediate left.

And our trench line, with its infinity of
salients and re-entrants, is itself only part of
the great salient of "Wipers." You may
imagine with what methodical solemnity the
Boche "crumps" the interior of that constricted area. Looking round at night, when
the star-shells float up over the skyline, one
could almost imagine one's self inside a complete circle, instead of a horse-shoe.

The machine - gunners of both sides are
extremely busy. In the plains of France the
pursuit of their nefarious trade was practically
limited to front-line work. When they did
venture to indulge in what they called " overhead " fire, their friends in the forefront used
to summon them after the performance, and
reproachfully point out sundry ominous rents
and abrasions in the back of the front-line

parapet. But here they can withdraw behind
a convenient ridge, and *strafe* Boches a mile
and a half away, without causing any com-
plaints. Needless to say, Brother Boche is
not backward in returning the compliment.
He has one gun in particular which never
tires in its efforts to rouse us from *ennui*. It
must be a long way off, for we can only just
hear the report. Moreover, its contribution
to our liveliness, when it does arrive, falls at
an extremely steep angle—so steep, indeed,
that it only just clears the back of the
embankment under which we live, and falls
upon the very doorsteps of the dug-outs with
which that sanctuary is honeycombed.

This invigorating shower is turned on
regularly for ten minutes, at three, six, nine,
and twelve o'clock daily. (Methodical regu-
larity is the most lovable feature of the
German character.) Its area of activity
includes our tiny but, alas! steadily growing
cemetery. One evening a regiment which had
recently "taken over" selected six P.M. as a
suitable hour for a funeral. The result was
a grimly humorous spectacle—the mourners,
including the Commanding Officer and officiating clergy, taking hasty cover in a truly novel

trench ; while the central figure of the ob-
sequies, sublimely indifferent to the Hun and
all his frightfulness, lay on the grass outside,
calm and impassive amid the whispering hail
of bullets.

As for the trenches themselves—well, in
the first place, there is no settled trench line
at all. The Salient has been a battlefield
for twelve months past. No one has ever had
the time, or opportunity, to construct anything
in the shape of permanent defences. A shallow
trench, trimmed with an untidy parapet of
sandbags, and there is your stronghold ! For
rest and meditation, a hole in the ground,
half-full of water and roofed with a sheet of
galvanised iron ; or possibly a glorified rabbit-
burrow in a canal-bank. These things, as a
modern poet has observed, are all right in the
summer-time. But winter here is a disinte-
grating season. It rains heavily for, say,
three days. Two days of sharp frost succeed,
and the rain-soaked earth is reduced to the
necessary degree of friability. Another day's
rain, and trenches and dug-outs come sliding
down like melted butter. Even if you revet
the trenches, it is not easy to drain them.
The only difference is that if your line is

situated on the forward slope of a hill the
support trench drains into the firing trench;
if they are on the reverse slope, the firing
trench drains into the support trench. Our
indefatigable friends Box and Cox, of the
Royal Engineers, assisted by sturdy Pioneer
Battalions, labour like heroes; but the utmost they can achieve, in a low-lying country
like this, is to divert as much water as
possible into some other Brigade's area.
Which they do, right cunningly.

In addition to the Boche, we wage continuous warfare with the elements, and the
various departments of Olympus render us
characteristic assistance. The Round Game
Department has issued a set of rules for the
correct method of massaging and greasing the
feet. (Major Wagstaffe refers to this as *Sole-
slapping; or What to do in the Children's
Hour: complete in Twelve Fortnightly Parts.*)
The Fairy Godmother Department presents
us with what the Quartermaster describes as
" Boots, gum, thigh "; and there has also
been an issue of so-called fur jackets, in which
the Practical Joke Department has plainly
taken a hand. Most of these garments appear
to have been contributed by animals unknown

to zoology, or more probably by a syndicate thereof. Corporal Mucklewame's costume gives him the appearance of a St Bernard dog with Astrakhan fore-legs. Sergeant Carfrae is attired in what looks like the skin of Nana, the dog-nurse in *Peter Pan*. Private Nigg, an undersized youth of bashful disposition, creeps forlornly about his duties disguised as an imitation leopard. As he passes by, facetious persons pull what is left of his tail. Private Tosh, on being confronted with his winter *trousseau*, observed bitterly—

" I jined the Airmy for tae be a sojer ; but I doot they must pit me doon as a mountain goat ! "

Still, though our variegated pelts cause us to resemble an unsuccessful compromise between Esau and an Eskimo, they keep our bodies warm. We wish we could say the same for our feet. On good days we stand ankle-deep ; on bad, we are occasionally over the knees. Thrice blessed then are our Boots, Gum, Thigh, though even these cannot altogether ward off frost - bite and chilblains.

Over the way, Brother Boche is having a bad time of it : his trenches are in a worse state than ours. Last night a plaintive voice cried out—

"Are you dere, Jock? Haf you whiskey? We haf plenty water!"

Not bad for a Boche, the platoon decided.

There is no doubt that whatever the German Great General Staff may think about the war and the future, the German Infantry soldier is "fed-up." His satiety takes the form of a craving for social intercourse with the foe. In the small hours, when the vigilance of the German N.C.O.'s is relaxed, and the officers are probably in their dug-outs, he makes rather pathetic overtures. We are frequently invited to come out and shake hands. "Dis war will be ober the nineteen of nex' month!" (Evidently the Kaiser has had another revelation.) The other morning a German soldier, with a wisp of something white in his hand, actually clambered out of the firing trench and advanced towards our lines. The distance was barely seventy yards. No shot was fired, but you may be sure that safety-catches were hastily released. Suddenly, in the tense silence, the ambassador's nerve failed him. He bolted back, followed by a few desultory bullets. The

reason for his sudden panic was never rightly
ascertained, but the weight of public opinion
inclined to the view that Mucklewame, who
had momentarily exposed himself above the
parapet, was responsible.

"I doot he thocht ye were a lion escapit
from the Scottish Zoo!" explained a brother
corporal, referring to his indignant colleague's
new winter coat.

Here is another incident, with a different
ending. At one point our line approaches to
within fifteen yards of the Boche trenches.
One wet and dismal dawn, as the battalion
stood to arms in the neighbourhood of this
delectable spot, there came a sudden shout
from the enemy, and an outburst of rapid
rifle fire. Almost simultaneously two breath-
less and unkempt figures tumbled over our
parapet into the firing trench. The fusilade
died away.

To the extreme discomfort and shame of
a respectable citizen of Bannockburn, one
Private Buncle, the more hairy of the two
visitors, upon recovering his feet, promptly
flung his arms around his neck and kissed him
on both cheeks. The outrage was repeated,
by his companion, upon Private Nigg. At

the same time both visitors broke into a
joyous chant of " Russky ! Russky ! " They
were escaped Russian prisoners.

When taken to Headquarters they explained that they had been brought up to
perform fatigue work near the German
trenches, and had seized upon a quiet moment
to slip into some convenient undergrowth.
Later, under cover of night, they had made
their way in the direction of the firing line,
arriving just in time to make a dash before
daylight discovered them. You may imagine
their triumphal departure from our trenches
—loaded with cigarettes, chocolate, biscuits,
buttons, bully beef, and other imperishable
souvenirs.

We have had other visitors. One bright
day a Boche aeroplane made a reconnaissance
of our lines. It was a beautiful thing, white
and birdlike. But as its occupants were probably taking photographs of our most secret
fastnesses, artistic appreciation was dimmed
by righteous wrath—wrath which turned to
profound gratification when a philistine
British plane appeared in the blue and
engaged the glittering stranger in battle.
There was some pretty aerial manœuvring,

right over our heads, as the combatants
swooped and circled for position. We could
hear their machine-gun pattering away; and
the volume of sound was increased by the
distant contributions of "Coughing Clara"—
our latest anti-aircraft gun, which appears to
suffer from chronic irritation of the mucous
membrane.

Suddenly the German aeroplane gave a
lurch; then righted herself; then began to
circle down, making desperate efforts to cross
the neutral line. But the British airman
headed her off. Next moment she lurched
again, and then took a "nose-dive" straight
into the British trenches. She fell on open
ground, a few hundred yards behind our
second line. The place had been a wilderness
a moment before; but the crowd which
instantaneously sprang up round the wreck
could not have been less than two hundred
strong. (One observes the same uncanny
phenomenon in London, when a cab-horse falls
down in a deserted street.) However, it
melted away at the rebuke of the first officer
who hurried to the spot, the process of dis-
solution being accelerated by several bursts of
German shrapnel.

Both pilot and observer were dead. They had made a gallant fight, and were buried the same evening, with all honour, in the little cemetery, alongside many who had once been their foes, but were now peacefully neutral.

## IV.

The housing question in Belgium confronts us with several novel problems. It is not so easy to billet troops here, especially in the Salient, as in France. Some of us live in huts, others in tents, others in dug-outs. Others, more fortunate, are loaded on to a fleet of motor-buses and whisked off to more civilised dwellings many miles away. These buses once plied for hire upon the streets of London. Each bus is in charge of the identical pair of cross-talk comedians who controlled its destinies in more peaceful days. Strangely attired in khaki and sheepskin, they salute officers with cheerful *bonhomie,* and bellow to one another throughout the journey the simple and primitive jests of their previous incarnation, to the huge delight of their fares.

The destination-boards and advertisements

are no more, for the buses are painted a neutral green all over; but the conductor is always ready and willing to tell you what his previous route was.

"That Daimler behind you, sir," he informs you, "is one of the Number Nineteens. Set you down at the top of Sloane Street many a time, I'll be bound. Ernie"— this to the driver, along the side of the bus — "you oughter have slowed down when that copper waved his little flag: he wasn't pleased with yer, ole son!" (The "copper" is a military mounted policeman, controlling the traffic of a little town which lies on our way to the trenches.) "This one we are on is a Number Eight, sir. No, that dent in the staircase wasn't done by no shell. The ole girl got that through a skid up against a lamp-post, one wet Saturday night in the Vauxhall Bridge Road. Dangerous place, London!"

We rattle through a brave little town, which is "carrying on" in the face of paralysed trade and periodical shelling. Soldiers abound. All are muddy, but some are muddier than others. The latter are going up to the trenches, the former are coming back. Upon the walls, here and there, we notice a gay poster advertising

an entertainment organised by certain Divisional troops, which is to be given nightly
throughout the week. At the foot of the
bill is printed in large capitals, A HOOGE
SUCCESS! We should like to send a
copy of that plucky document to Brother
Boche. He would not understand it, but it
would annoy him greatly.

Now we leave the town behind, and quicken
up along the open road — an interminable
ribbon of *pavé*, absolutely straight, and bor-
dered upon either side by what was once
macadam, but is now a quagmire a foot deep.
Occasionally there is a warning cry of "Wire!"
and the outside fares hurriedly bow from the
waist, in order to avoid having their throats
cut by a telephone wire — "Gunners, for a
dollar!" surmises a strangled voice—tightly
stretched across the road between two poplars.
Occasionally, too, that indefatigable humourist, Ernie, directs his course beneath some low-
spreading branches, through which the upper
part of the bus crashes remorselessly, while
the passengers, lying sardinewise upon the
roof, uplift their voices in profane and blood-
thirsty chorus.

"Nothing like a bit o' fun on the way to

the trenches, boys! It may be the last you'll get!" is the only apology which Ernie offers.

Presently our vehicle bumps across a nubbly bridge, and enters what was once a fair city. It is a walled city, like Chester, and is separated from the surrounding country by a moat as wide as the upper Thames. In days gone by those ramparts and that moat could have held an army at bay—and probably did, more than once. They have done so yet again; but at what a cost!

We glide through the ancient gateway and along the ghostly streets, and survey the crowning achievement of the cultured Boche. The great buildings — the Cathedral, the Cloth Hall — are jagged ruins. The fronts of the houses have long disappeared, leaving the interiors exposed to view, like a doll's house. Here is a street full of shops. That heap of splintered wardrobes and legless tables was once a furniture warehouse. That snug little corner house, with the tottering zinc counter and the twisted beer engine, is an obvious estaminet. You may observe the sign, *Aux Deux Amis*, in dingy lettering over the door-

C

way. Here is an oil-and-colour shop: you can still see the red ochre and white-lead splashed about among the ruins.

In almost every house the ceilings of the upper floors have fallen in. Chairs, tables, and bedsteads hang precariously into the room below. Here and there a picture still adheres to the wall. From one of the bedposts flutters a tattered and diminutive garment of blue and white check—some little girl's frock. Where is that little girl now, we wonder; and has she got another frock?

One is struck above all things with the minute detail of the damage. You would say that a party of lunatics had been let loose on the city with coal-hammers: there is hardly a square yard of any surface which is not pierced, or splintered, or dented. The whole fabric of the place lies prostrate, under a shroud of broken bricks and broken plaster. The Hun has said in his majesty: "If you will not yield me this, the last city in the last corner of Belgium, I can at least see to it that not one stone thereof remains upon another. So—yah!"

Such is the appearance presented by the venerable and historic city of Ypres, after fifteen months of personal contact with the apostles of the new civilisation. Only the methodical and painstaking Boche could have reduced a town of such a size to such a state. Imagine Chester in a similar condition, and you may realise the number of shells which have fallen, and are still falling, into the stricken city.

But—the main point to observe is this. We are inside, and the Boche is outside! Fenced by a mighty crescent of prosaic trenches, themselves manned by paladins of an almost incredible stolidity, Ypres still points her broken fingers to the sky—shattered, silent, but inviolate still; and all owing to the obstinacy of a dull and unready nation which merely keeps faith and stands by its friends. Such an attitude of mind is incomprehensible to the Boche, and we are well content that it should be so.

# CHAPTER TWO.

## "SHELL OUT!"

THIS, according to our latest subaltern from home, is the title of a *revue* which is running in Town; but that is a mere coincidence. The entertainment to which I am now referring took place in Flanders, and the leading parts were assigned to distinguished members of "K (1)."

The scene was the Chateau de Grandbois, or some other kind of Bois; possibly Vert. Not that we called it that: we invariably referred to it afterwards as Hush Hall, for reasons which will be set forth in due course.

One morning, while sojourning in what Olympus humorously calls a rest camp—a collection of antiquated wigwams half submerged in a mud-flat intermittently shelled —we received the intelligence that we were

to extricate ourselves forthwith, and take
over a fresh sector of trenches. The news
was doubly unwelcome, because, in the first
place, it is always unpleasant to face the
prospect of trenches of any kind; and
secondly, to take over strange trenches in
the dead of a winter night is an experience which borders upon nightmare — the
hot lobster and toasted cheese variety.

The opening stages of this enterprise are
almost ambassadorial in their formality. First
of all, the Brigade Staff which is coming in
visits the Headquarters of the Brigade which
is going out—usually a chateau or farm somewhere in rear of the trenches—and makes the
preliminary arrangements. After that the
Commanding Officers and Company Commanders of the incoming battalions visit their
own particular section of the line. They are
shown over the premises by the outgoing
tenants, who make little or no attempt to
conceal their satisfaction at the expiration of
their lease. The Colonels and the Captains
then return to camp, with depressing tales of
crumbling parapets, noisome dug-outs, and
positions open to enfilade.

On the day of the relief various advance

parties go up, keeping under the lee of hedges
and embankments, and marching in single
file. (At least, that is what they are supposed to do. If not ruthlessly shepherded,
they will advance in fours along the skyline.)
Having arrived, they take over such positions
as can be relieved by daylight in comparative
safety. They also take over trench stores,
and exchange trench gossip. The latter is a
fearsome and uncanny thing. It usually
begins life at the "refilling point," where the
A.S.C. motor-lorries dump down next day's
rations, and the regimental transport picks
it up.

An A.S.C. sergeant mentions casually to a
regimental Quartermaster that he has heard
it said at the Supply Depôt that heavy firing
has been going on in the Channel. The
Quartermaster, on returning to the Transport
Lines, observes to his Quartermaster-Sergeant
that the German Fleet has come out at last.
The Quartermaster-Sergeant, when he meets
the ration parties behind the lines that night,
announces to a platoon sergeant that we have
won a great naval victory. The platoon
sergeant, who is suffering from trench feet
and is a constant reader of a certain pessi-

mistic halfpenny journal, replies gloomily:
"We'll have had heavy losses oorselves, too,
I doot!" This observation is overheard by
various members of the ration party. By
midnight several hundred yards of the firing
line know for a fact that there has been a
naval disaster of the first magnitude off the
coast of a place which every one calls Gally
Polly, and that the whole of our Division are
to be transferred forthwith to the Near East
to stem the tide of calamity.

Still, we must have *something* to chat about.

Meanwhile Brigade Majors and Adjutants,
holding a stumpy pencil in one hand and a
burning brow in the other, are composing
Operation Orders which shall effect the relief,
without—

(1) Leaving some detail—the bombers, or
the snipers, or the sock-driers, or the pea-soup
experts—unrelieved altogether.

(2) Causing relievers and relieved to meet
violently together in some constricted fairway.

(3) Trespassing into some other Brigade
Area. (This is far more foolhardy than to
wander into the German lines.)

(4) Getting shelled.

Pitfall Number One is avoided by keeping a permanent and handy list of "all the people who do funny things on their own" (as the vulgar throng call the "specialists"), and checking it carefully before issuing Orders.

Number Two is dealt with by issuing a strict time-table, which might possibly be adhered to by a well-drilled flock of archangels, in broad daylight, upon good roads, and under peace conditions.

Number Three is provided for by copious and complicated map references.

Number Four is left to Providence—and is usually the best-conducted feature of the excursion.

Under cover of night the Battalion sets out, in comparatively small parties. They form a strange procession. The men wear their trench costume—thigh-boots (which do not go well with a kilt), variegated coats of skins, and woollen nightcaps. Stuffed under their belts and through their packs they carry newspapers, broken staves for firewood, parcels from home, and sandbags loaded with mysterious comforts. A dilapidated parrot and a few goats are all that is required to complete the picture of Robinson Crusoe changing camp.

Progress is not easy. It is a pitch-black night. By day, this road (and all the countryside) is a wilderness: nothing more innocent ever presented itself to the eye of an inquisitive aeroplane. But after nightfall it is packed with troops and transport, and not a light is shown. If you can imagine what the Mansion House crossing would be like if called upon to sustain its midday traffic at midnight—the Mansion House crossing entirely unilluminated, paved with twelve inches of liquid mud, intersected by narrow strips of *pavé*, and liberally pitted with "crump-holes"— you may derive some faint idea of the state of things at a busy road-junction lying behind the trenches.

Until reaching what is facetiously termed "the shell area"—as if any spot in this benighted district were not a shell area— the troops plod along in fours at the right of the road. If they can achieve two miles an hour, they do well. At any moment they may be called upon to halt, and crowd into the roadside, while a transport-train passes carrying rations, and coke, and what is called

"R.E. material"—this may be anything from a bag of nails to steel girders nine feet long— up to the firing line. When this procession, consisting of a dozen limbered waggons, drawn by four mules and headed by a profane person on horseback — the Transport Officer — has rumbled past, the Company, which has been standing respectfully in the ditch enjoying a refreshing shower-bath of mud, and hoping that none of the steel girders are projecting from the limber more than a yard or two, sets out once more upon its way—only to take hasty cover again as sounds of fresh and more ani-mated traffic are heard approaching from the opposite direction. There is no mistaking the nature of this cavalcade : the long vista of glowing cigarette-ends tells an unmistakable tale. These are artillery waggons, returning empty from replenishing the batteries; scatter-ing homely jests like hail, and proceeding, wherever possible, at a hand-gallop. He is a cheery and gallant soul the R.A. driver, but his interpretation of the rules of the road requires drastic revision.

Sometimes an axle breaks, or a waggon side-slips off the *pavé* into the morass reserved for infantry, and overturns. The result is a block, which promptly extends forward and back for a couple of miles. A peculiarly British chorus of inquiry and remonstrance— a blend of biting sarcasm and blasphemous humour—surges up and down the line; until plunging mules are unyoked, and the offending vehicle man-handled out of sight into the inky blackness by the roadside; or, in extreme cases, is annihilated with axes. Everything has to make way for a ration train. To crown all, it is more than likely that the calmness and smooth working of the proceedings will be assisted by a burst of shrapnel overhead. It is a most amazing scrimmage altogether. One of those members of His Majesty's Opposition who are doing so much at present to save our country from destruction, by kindly pointing out the mistakes of the British Government and the British Army, would refer to the whole scene as a pandemonium of mismanagement and ineptitude. And yet, though the scene is enacted night after night without a break, there is hardly a case on record of the transport being surprised upon these roads by the coming of daylight, and none whatever of the rations and ammunition failing to get through.

It is difficult to imagine that Brother Boche, who on the other side of that ring of star-shells is conducting a precisely similar undertaking, is able, with all his perfect organisation and cast-iron methods, to achieve a result in any way superior to that which Thomas Atkins reaches by rule of thumb and sheer force of character.

At length the draggled Company worms its way through the press to the fringe of the shell-area, beyond which no transport may pass. The distance of this point from the trenches varies considerably, and depends largely upon the caprice of the Boche. On this occasion, however, we still have a mile or two to go—across country now, in single file, at the heels of a guide from the battalion which we are relieving.

Guides may be divided into two classes—

(1) Guides who do not know the way, and say so at the outset.

(2) Guides who do not know the way, but leave it you to discover the fact.

There are no other kinds of guides.

The pace is down to a mile an hour now,

except in the case of men in the tail of the line, who are running rapidly. It is a curious but quite inexplicable fact that if you set a hundred men to march in single file in the dark, though the leading man may be crawling like a tortoise, the last man is compelled to proceed at a profane double if he is to avoid being left behind and lost.

Still, everybody gets there somehow, and in due course the various Company Commanders are enabled to telephone to their respective Battalion Headquarters the information that the Relief is completed. For this relief, much thanks!

After that the outgoing Battalion files slowly out, and the newcomers are left gloomily contemplating their new abiding-place, and observing—

"I wonder if there is *any* Division in the whole blessed Expeditionary Force, besides ours, which ever does a single dam thing to keep its trenches in repair!"

II.

All of which brings us back to Hush Hall, where the Headquarters of the outgoing Brigade are handing over to their successors.

Hush Hall, or the Chateau de Grandbois, is a modern country house, and once stood up white and gleaming in all its brave finery of stucco, conservatories, and ornamental lake, amid a pleasant wood not far from a main road. It is such a house as you might find round about Guildford or Hindhead. There are many in this fair countryside, but few are inhabited now, and none by their rightful owners. They are all marked on the map, and the Boche gunners are assiduous map-readers. Hush Hall has got off comparatively lightly. It is still habitable, and well furnished. The roof is demolished upon the side most exposed to the enemy, and many of the trees in the surrounding wood are broken and splintered by shrapnel. Still, provided the weather remains passable, one can live there. Upon the danger-side the windows are closed and shuttered. Weeds grow apace in the garden. No smoke emerges from the chimneys. (If it does, the Mess Corporal hears about it from the Staff Captain.) A few strands of barbed wire obstruct the passage of those careless or adventurous persons who may desire to explore the forbidden side of the house. The front door is bolted and barred: visitors, after approaching stealthily along the lee of a hedge, like travellers of dubious *bonâ fides* on a Sunday afternoon, enter unobtrusively by the back door, which is situated on the blind side of the chateau. Their path thereto is beset by imploring notices like the following :—

> THE SLIGHTEST MOVEMENT DRAWS SHELL FIRE. KEEP CLOSE TO THE HEDGE.

A later hand has added the following moving postscript :—

> WE LIVE HERE. YOU DON'T !

It was the Staff Captain who was responsible for the re-christening of the establishment.

"What sort of place is this new palace we are going to doss in?" inquired the Machine-Gun Officer, when the Staff Captain returned from his preliminary visit.

The Staff Captain, who was a man of few words, replied—

"It's the sort of shanty where everybody goes about in felt slippers, saying 'Hush!'"

Brigade Headquarters — this means the Brigadier, the Brigade Major, the Staff Captain, the Machine-Gun Officer, the Signal Officer, mayhap a Padre and a Liaison Officer, accompanied by a mixed multitude of clerks, telegraphists, and scullions— arrived safely at their new quarters under cover of night, and were hospitably received by the outgoing tenants, who had finished their evening meal and were girded up for departure. In fact, the Machine-Gun Officer, Liaison Officer, and Padre had already gone, leaving their seniors to hold the fort till the last. The Signal Officer was down in the cellar, handing over ohms, ampères, short-circuits, and other mysterious trench stores to his "opposite number."

Upon these occasions there is usually a good deal of time to fill in between the arrival of the new brooms and the departure of the old. This period of waiting may be

likened to that somewhat anxious interval
with which frequenters of racecourses are
familiar, between the finish of the race and
the announcement of the "All Right!" The
outgoing Headquarters are waiting for the
magic words — "Relief Complete!" Until
that message comes over the buzzer, the
period of tension endures. The main point
of difference is that the gentleman who has
staked his fortune on the legs of a horse
has only to wait a few minutes for the con-
firmation of his hopes; while a Brigadier,
whose bedtime (or even breakfast - time) is
at the mercy of an errant platoon, may
have to sit up all night.

"Sit down and make yourselves comfortable," said A Brigade to X Brigade.

X Brigade complied, and having been furnished with refreshment, led off with the
inevitable question—

"Does one—er—get shelled much here?"

There was a reassuring coo from A Brigade.

"Oh, no. This is a very healthy spot.
One has to be careful, of course. No movement, or fires, or anything of that kind. A
sentry or two, to warn people against approaching over the open by day, and you'll

D

be as cooshie as anything!" ("Cooshie" is
the latest word here. That and "crump.")

"I ought to warn you of one thing," said
the Brigadier. "Owing to the surrounding
woods, sound is most deceptive here. You
will hear shell-bursts which appear quite close,
when in reality they are quite a distance away.
That, for instance!"—as a shell exploded apparently just outside the window. "That
little fellow is a couple of hundred yards
away, in the corner of the wood. The Boche
has been groping about there for a battery
for the last two days."

"Is the battery there?" inquired a voice.

"No; it is further east. But there is a
Gunner's Mess about two hundred yards from
here, in that house which you passed on the
way up."

"Oh!" observed X Brigade.

Gunners are peculiar people. When pro-
fessionally engaged, no men could be more
retiring. They screen their operations from
the public gaze with the utmost severity,
shrouding batteries in screens of foliage and
other rustic disguises. If a layman strays
anywhere near one of these arboreal retreats,
a gunner thrusts out a visage inflamed with

righteous wrath, and curses him for giving the position away. But in his hours of relaxation the gunner is a different being. He billets himself in a house with plenty of windows: he illuminates all these by night, and hangs washing therefrom by day. When inclined for exercise, he plays football upon an open space labelled—*Not to be used by troops during daylight*. Therefore, despite his technical excellence and superb courage, he is an uncomfortable neighbour for establishments like Hush Hall.

In this respect he offers a curious contrast to the Sapper. Off duty, the Sapper is the most unobtrusive of men—a cave-man, in fact. He burrows deep into the earth or the side of a hill, and having secured the roof of this cavern against direct hits by ingenious contrivances of his own manufacture, constructs a suite of furniture of a solid and enduring pattern, and lives the life of a comfortable recluse. But when engaged in the pursuit of his calling, the Sapper is the least retiring of men. The immemorial tradition of the great Corps to which he belongs has ordained that no fire, however fierce, must be allowed to interfere with a Sapper in the execution of his duty. This rule is usually interpreted by the Sapper to mean that you must not perform your allotted task under cover when it is possible to do so under fire. To this is added, as a rider, that in the absence of an adequate supply of fire, you must draw fire. So the Sapper walks cheerfully about on the tops of parapets, hugging large and conspicuous pieces of timber, or clashing together sheets of corrugated iron, as happy as a king.

" You will find this house quite snug," continued the Brigadier. "The eastern suite is to be avoided, because there is no roof there; and if it rains outside for a day, it rains in the best bedroom for a week. There is a big kitchen in the basement, with a capital range. That's all, I think. The chief thing to avoid is movement of any kind. The leaves are coming off the trees now——"

At this moment an orderly entered the room with a pink telegraph message.

"Relief complete, sir!" announced the Brigade Major, reading it.

"Good work!" replied both Brigadiers, looking at their watches simultaneously, "considering the state of the country." The Brigadier of "A" rose to his feet.

"Now we can pass along quietly," he said. "Good luck to you. By the way, take care of Edgar, won't you? Any little attention which you can show him will be greatly appreciated."

"Who is Edgar?"

"Oh, I thought the Staff Captain would have told you. Edgar is the swan—the last of his race, I'm afraid, so far as this place is concerned. He lives on the lake, and usually comes ashore to draw his rations about lunchtime. He is inclined to be stand-offish on one side, as he has only one eye; but he is most affable on the other. Well, now to find our horses!"

As the three officers departed down the back-door steps, a hesitating voice followed them—

"H'm! Is there any place where one can go—a cellar, or any old spot of that kind —just in case we are——"

"Bless you, you'll be all right!" was the cheery reply. (The outgoing Brigade is always excessively cheery.) "But there are dug-outs over there—in the garden. They haven't been occupied for some months, so you may find them a bit ratty. You won't require them, though. Good night!"

## III.

*Whizz! Boom! Bang! Crash! Wump!*

"It's just as well," mused the Brigade Major, turning in his sleep about three o'clock the following morning, "that they warned us about the deceptive sound of the shelling here. One would almost imagine that it was quite close. . . . That last one was heavy stuff: it shook the whole place! . . . This is a topping mattress: it would be rotten having to take to the woods again after getting into really cooshie quarters at last. . . . There they go again!" as a renewed tempest of shells rent the silence of night. "That old battery must be getting it in the neck! . . . Hallo, I could have sworn something hit the roof that time! A loose slate, I expect! Anyhow . . ."

The Brigade Major, who had had a very long day, turned over and went to sleep again.

## IV.

The next morning, a Sunday, broke bright and clear. Contrary to his usual habit, the

Brigade Major took a stroll in the garden before breakfast. The first object which caught his eye, as he came down the back-door steps, was the figure of the Staff Captain, brooding pensively over a large crater, close to the hedge. The Brigade Major joined him.

"I wonder if that was there yesterday!" he observed, referring to the crater.

"Couldn't have been," growled the Staff Captain. "We walked to the house along this very hedge. No craters then!"

"True!" agreed the Brigade Major amiably. He turned and surveyed the garden. "That lawn looks a bit of a golf course. What lovely bunkers!"

"They appear to be quite new, too," remarked the Staff Captain thoughtfully. "Come to breakfast!"

On their way back they found the Brigadier, the Machine-Gun Officer, and the Padre gazing silently upward.

"I wonder when that corner of the house got knocked off," the M.G.O. was observing.

"Fairly recently, I should say," replied the Brigadier.

"Those marks beside your bedroom window, sir—they look pretty fresh!" interpolated the Padre, a sincere but somewhat tactless Christian.

Brigade Headquarters regarded one another with dubious smiles.

" I *wonder*," began a tentative voice, " if those fellows last night were indulging in a leg-pull—what is called in this country a *tire-jambe*—when they assured us——"

WHOO-OO-OO-OO-UMP !

A shell came shrieking over the tree-tops, and fell with a tremendous splash into the geometrical centre of the lake, fifty yards away.

For the next two hours, shrapnel, whizz-bangs, Silent Susies, and other explosive wild-fowl raged round the walls of Hush Hall. The inhabitants thereof, some twenty persons in all, were gathered in various apartments on the lee side.

" It is still possible," remarked the Briga-dier, lighting his pipe, " that they are not aim-ing at us. However, it is just as inconvenient to be buried by accident as by design. As soon as the first direct hit is registered upon this imposing fabric, we will retire to the dug-outs. Send word to the kitchen that every

one is to be ready to clear out of the house
when necessary.

Next moment there came a resounding
crash, easily audible above the tornado raging
in the garden, followed by the sound of
splintering glass. Hush Hall rocked. The
Mess waiter appeared.

"A shell has just came in through the
dining-room window, sirr," he informed the
Mess President, "and broke three of they
new cups!"

"How tiresome!" said the Brigadier.
"Dug-outs, everybody!"


V.

There were no casualties, which was rather
miraculous. Late in the afternoon Brigade
Headquarters ventured upon another stroll in
the garden. The tumult had ceased, and
the setting Sabbath sun glowed peacefully
upon the battered countenance of Hush Hall.
The damage was not very extensive, for the
house was stoutly built. Still, two bedrooms,
recently occupied, were a wreck of broken
glass and splintered plaster, while the gravel

outside was littered with lead sheeting and twisted chimney-cans. The shell which had aroused the indignation of the Mess waiter by entering the dining-room window, had in reality hit the ground directly beneath it. Six feet higher, and the Brigadier's order to clear the house would have been entirely superfluous.

The Brigade Major and the Staff Captain surveyed the unruffled surface of the lake—a haunt of ancient peace in the rays of the setting sun. Upon the bosom thereof floated a single, majestic, one-eyed swan, performing intricate toilet exercises. It was Edgar.

"He must have a darned good dug-out somewhere!" observed the Brigade Major enviously.

# CHAPTER THREE.

### WINTER SPORTS : VARIOUS.

HUSH HALL having become an even less desirable place of residence than had hitherto been thought possible, Headquarters very sensibly sent for their invaluable friends, Box and Cox, of the Royal Engineers, and requested that they would proceed to make the place proof against shells and weather, forthwith, if not sooner.

Those phlegmatic experts made a thorough investigation of the resources of the establishment, and departed mysteriously, after the fashion of the common plumber of civilisation, into space. Three days later they returned, accompanied by a horde of acolytes, who, with characteristic contempt for the pathetic appeals upon the notice-boards, proceeded to dump down lumber, sandbags, and corrugated-iron roofing in the most exposed portions of the garden.

This done, some set out to shore up the ceilings of the basement with mighty battens of wood, and to convert that region into a nest of cunningly devised bedrooms. Others reinforced the flooring above with a layer of earth and brick rubble three feet deep. On the top of all this they relaid not only the original floor, but eke the carpet.

"The only difference from before, sir," explained Box to the admiring Staff Captain, "is that people will have to walk up three steps to get into the dining-room now, instead of going in on the level."

"I wonder what the Marquise de Grandbois will think of it all when she returns to her ancestral home," mused the Staff Captain.

"If anything," maintained the invincible Box, "we have improved it for her. For example, she can now light the chandelier without standing on a chair—without getting up from table, in fact! However, to resume. The fireplace, you will observe, has not been touched. I have left a sort of well in the floor all round it, lined with some stuff I found in Mademoiselle's room. At least," added Box coyly, " I think it must have been Mademoiselle's room! You can sit in the well every evening after supper. The walls of this room "—prodding the same— "are lined with sandbags, covered with tapestry. Pretty artistic—what?"

"Extremely," agreed the Staff Captain. "You will excuse my raising the point, I know, but can the apartment now be regarded as shell-proof?"

"Against everything but a direct hit. I wouldn't advise you to sleep in this room much, but you could have your meals here all right. Then, if the Boche starts putting over heavy stuff, you can pop down into the basement and have your dessert in bed. You'll be absolutely safe there. In fact, the more the house tumbles down the safer you will be. It will only make your protection shell thicker. So if you hear heavy thuds overhead, don't be alarmed!"

"I won't," promised the Staff Captain. "I shall lie in bed, drinking a nice hot cup of tea, and wondering whether the last crash was the kitchen chimney, or only the drawing-room piano coming down another storey. Now show me my room."

"We have had to put you in the larder," explained Box apologetically, as he steered his guest through a forest of struts with an electric torch. "At least, I think it's the larder : it has a sort of meaty smell. The General is in the dairy—a lovely little suite, with white tiles. The Brigade Major has the scullery : it has a sink, so is practically as good as a flat in Park Place. I have run up cubicles for the others in the kitchen. Here is your little cot. It is only six feet by four, but you can dress in the garden."

"It's a *sweet* little nest, dear!" replied the Staff Captain, quite hypnotised by this time. "I'll just get my maid to put me into something loose, and then I'll run along to your room, and we'll have a nice cosy gossip together before dinner!"

In due course we removed our effects from the tottering and rat-ridden dug-outs in which we had taken sanctuary during the shelling, and prepared to settle down for the winter in our new quarters.

"We might be *very* much worse off!" we observed the first evening, listening to the comfortably muffled sounds of shells overhead.

And we were right. Three days later we received an intimation from the Practical Joke Department that we were to evacuate our present sector of trenches (including Hush Hall) forthwith, and occupy another part of the line.

In all Sports, Winter and Summer, the supremacy of the Practical Joke Department is unchallenged.

## II.

Meanwhile, up in the trenches, the combatants are beguiling the time in their several ways.

Let us take the reserve line first—the lair of Battalion Headquarters and its appurtenances. Much of our time here, as elsewhere, is occupied in unostentatious retirement to our dug-outs, to avoid the effects of a bombardment. But a good amount—an increasing amount—of it is devoted to the contemplation of our own shells bursting over the Boche trenches. Gone are the days during which we used to sit close and "stick it out," consoling ourselves with the vague hope that

by the end of the week our gunners might
possibly have garnered sufficient ammunition
to justify a few brief hours' retaliation. The
boot is on the other leg now. For every
Boche battery that opens on us, two or three
of ours thunder back a reply—and that without any delays other than those incidental to
the use of that maddening instrument, the
field-telephone. During the past six months
neither side has been able to boast much in
the way of ground actually gained ; but the
moral ascendancy—the initiative—the offensive — call it what you will — has changed
hands ; and no one knows it better than the
Boche. We are the attacking party now.

The trenches in this country are not arranged
with such geometric precision as in France.
For instance, the reserve line is not always
connected with the firing lines by a communication trench. Those persons whose duty
it is to pay daily visits to the fire-trenches—
Battalion Commanders, Gunner and Sapper
officers, an occasional Staff Officer, and an
occasional most devoted Padre—perform the
journey as best they may. Sometimes they
skirt a wood or hedge, sometimes they keep
under the lee of an embankment, sometimes

they proceed across the open, with the stealthy caution of persons playing musical chairs, ready to sit down in the nearest shell-crater the moment the music—in the form of a visitation of " whizz-bangs "—strikes up.

It is difficult to say which kind of weather is least favourable to this enterprise. On sunny days one's movements are visible to Boche observers upon adjacent summits; while on foggy days the Boche gunners, being able to see nothing at all, amuse themselves by generous and unexpected contributions of shrapnel in all directions. Stormy weather is particularly unpleasant, for the noise of the wind in the trees makes it difficult to hear the shell approaching. Days of heavy rain are the most desirable on the whole, for then the gunners are too busy bailing out their gun-pits to worry their heads over adventurous pedestrians. One learns, also, to mark down and avoid particular danger-spots. For instance, the south-east corner of that wood, where a reserve company are dug in, is visited by " Silent Susans " for about five minutes each noontide : it is therefore advisable to select some other hour for one's daily visit. (Silent Susan, by the way, is not a

E

desirable member of the sex. Owing to her
intensely high velocity she arrives overhead
without a sound, and then bursts with a
perfectly stunning detonation and a shower of
small shrapnel bullets.) There is a fixed rifle-
battery, too, which fires all day long, a shot at
a time, down the main street of the ruined
and deserted village named Vrjoozlehem,
through which one must pass on the way
to the front - line trenches. Therefore in
negotiating this delectable spot, one shapes
a laborious course through a series of back-
yards and garden-plots, littered with broken
furniture and brick rubble, allowing the rifle
bullets the undisputed use of the street.

The mention of Vrjoozlehem — that is not
its real name, but a simplified form of it—
brings to our notice the wholesale and whole-
hearted fashion in which the British Army
has taken Belgian institutions under its wing.
Nomenclature, for instance. In France we
make no attempt to interfere with this : we
content ourselves with devising a pronounce-
able variation of the existing name. For
example, if a road is called La Rue du Bois,
we simply call it " Roodiboys," and leave it
at that. On the same principle, Etaples is

modified to " Eatables," and Sailly-la-Bourse
to " Sally Booze." But in Belgium more
drastic procedure is required. A Scotsman is
accustomed to pronouncing difficult names,
but even he is unable to contend with words
composed almost entirely of the letters j, z,
and v. So our resourceful Ordnance Department has issued maps—admirable maps—upon
which the outstanding features of the landscape are marked in plain figures. But instead
of printing the original place-names, they put
" Moated Grange," or " Clapham Junction,"
or " Dead Dog Farm," which simplifies matters
beyond all possibility of error. (The system
was once responsible, though, for an unjust
if unintentional aspersion upon the character
of a worthy man. The C.O. of a certain battalion had occasion to complain to those above
him of the remissness of one of his chaplains.
"He's a lazy beggar, sir," he said. " Over
and over again I have told him to come up
and show himself in the front-line trenches, but
he never seems to be able to get past Leices-
ter Square ! ")

The naming of the trenches themselves has
been left largely to local enterprise. An
observant person can tell, by a study of the

numerous name-boards, which of his countrymen have been occupying the line during the
past six months. " Grainger Street " and
" Jesmond Dene " give direct evidence of
" Canny N'castle." "Sherwood Avenue" and
" Notts Forest " have a Midland flavour.
Lastly, no great mental effort is required
to decide who labelled two communication
trenches " The Gorbals " and " Coocaddens "
respectively !

Some names have obviously been bestowed
by officers, as " Sackville Street," " The Al-
bany," and " Burlington Arcade " denote.
" Pinch-Gut " and " Crab-Crawl " speak for
themselves. So does " Vermin Villa." Other
localities, again, have obviously been labelled
by persons endowed with a nice gift of irony.
" Sanctuary Wood " is the last place on earth
where any one would dream of taking sanctuary ; while " Lovers' Walk," which bounds it,
is the scene of almost daily expositions of the
choicest brand of Boche hate.

And so on. But one day, when the War is
over, and this mighty trench line is thrown
open to the disciples of the excellent Mr Cook
—as undoubtedly it will be—care should be
taken that these trench names are preserved

and perpetuated. It would be impossible to select a more characteristic and fitting memorial to the brave hearts who constructed them —too many of whom are sleeping their last sleep within a few yards of their own cheerful handiwork.

### III.

After this digression we at length reach the firing line. It is quite unlike anything of its kind that we have hitherto encountered. It is situated in what was once a thick wood. Two fairly well-defined trenches run through the undergrowth, from which the sentries of either side have been keeping relentless watch upon one another, night and day, for many months. The wood itself is a mere forest of poles : hardly a branch, and not a twig, has been spared by the shrapnel. In the No-man's-land between the trenches the poles have been reduced to mere stumps a few inches high.

It is behind the firing trench that the most unconventional scene presents itself. Strictly speaking, there ought to be—and generally is —a support-line some seventy yards in rear of

the first. This should be occupied by all
troops not required in the firing trench. But
the trench is empty—which is not altogether
surprising, considering that it is half-full of
water. Its rightful occupants are scattered
through the wood behind — in dug-outs, in
redoubts, or *en plein air*—cooking, washing,
or repairing their residences. The whole scene
suggests a gipsy encampment rather than a
fortified post. A hundred yards away, through
the trees, you can plainly discern the Boche
firing trench, and the Boche in that trench
can discern you: yet never a shot comes. It
is true that bullets are humming through the
air and glancing off trees, but these are mostly
due to the enterprise of distant machine-guns
and rifle-batteries, firing from some position
well adapted for enfilade. Frontal fire there
is little or none. In the front-line trenches, at
least, Brother Boche has had enough of it.
His motto now is, "Live and let live!" In
fact, he frequently makes plaintive state-
ments to that effect in the silence of night.
Especially the Saxons. Saxons have glim-
merings of humanity. The other night a
voice cried out to us—

"Don't shoot at us, Jock! Ve are der Saxons. Der Prussians vill be here on Vriday!"

You might think, then, that life in Willow Grove would be a tranquil affair. But if you look up among the few remaining branches of that tall tree in the centre of the wood, you may notice shreds of some material flapping in the breeze. Those are sandbags and part of a uniform—or were. Last night, within the space of one hour, seventy-three shells fell into this wood, and the first of them registered a direct hit upon the dug-out of which the sandbags formed part. There were eight men in that dug-out. The telephone-wires were broken in the first few minutes, and there was some delay before news of the bombardment could be transmitted back to Headquarters. Then our big guns far in rear spoke out, until the enemy's batteries (probably in response to an urgent appeal from their own front line) ceased firing. Thereupon "A" Company, who at Bobby Little's behest had taken immediate cover in the water-logged support-trench, returned stolidly to their open-air encampment in Willow Grove.

Death, when he makes the mistake of raiding your premises every day, loses most of his terrors and becomes a bit of a bore.

This morning the Company presents its normal appearance: its numbers have been reduced by eight—*c'est tout!* It may be some one else's turn to-morrow, but after all, that is what we are here for. Anyhow, we are keeping the Boches out of "Wipers," and a bit over. So we stretch our legs in the wood, and keep the flooded trench for the next emergency.

Let us approach a group of four which is squatting sociably round a small and inadequate fire of twigs, upon which four messtins are simmering. The quartette consists of Privates Cosh and Tosh, together with Privates Buncle and Nigg, preparing their midday meal.

"Tak' off yon damp chup, Jimmy," suggested Tosh to Buncle, who was officiating as stoker. "Ye mind what the Captain said aboot smoke?"

"It wasna the Captain: it was the Officer," rejoined Buncle cantankerously.

(It may here be explained, at the risk of another digression, that no length of association or degree of intimacy will render the average British soldier familiar with the names of his officers. The Colonel is "The C.O."; the Second in Command is "The Major"; your Company Commander is "The Captain," and your Platoon Commander "The Officer." As for all others of commissioned rank in the regiment, some twenty-four in all, they are as nought. With the exception of the Quartermaster, in whose shoes each member of the rank and file hopes one day to stand, they simply do not exist.)

"Onyway," pursued the careful Tosh, "he said that if any smoke was shown, all fires was tae be pitten oot. So mind and see no' to get a cauld dinner for us all, Jimmy!"

"Cauld or het," retorted the gentleman addressed, "it's little dinner I'll be gettin' this day! And ye ken fine why!" he added darkly.

Private Tosh removed a cigarette from his lower lip and sighed patiently.

"For the last time," he announced, with the air of a righteous man suffering long, "I did not lay ma hand on your dirrty wee bit ham!"

"Maybe," countered the bereaved Buncle

swiftly, "you did not lay your hand upon it; but you had it tae your breakfast for all that, Davie!"

"I never pit ma hand on it!" repeated Tosh doggedly.

"No? Then I doot you gave it a bit kick with your foot," replied the inflexible Buncle.

"Or got some other body tae luft it for him!" suggested Private Nigg, looking hard at Tosh's habitual accomplice, Cosh.

"I had it pitten in an auld envelope from hame, addressed with my name," continued the mourner. "It couldna hae got oot o' that by accident!"

"Weel," interposed Cosh, with forced geniality, "it's no a thing tae argie-bargie aboot. Whatever body lufted it, it's awa' by this time. It's a fine day, boys!"

This flagrant attempt to raise the conversation to a less controversial plane met with no encouragement. Private Buncle, refusing to be appeased, replied sarcastically—

"Aye, is it? And it was a fine nicht last nicht, especially when the shellin' was gaun on! Especially in number seeven dug-oot!"

There was a short silence. Number seven

dug-out was no more, and its late occupants were now lying under their waterproof
sheets, not a hundred yards away, waiting
for a Padre. Presently, however, the pacific
Cosh, who in his hours of leisure was addicted
to mild philosophical rumination, gave a fresh
turn to the conversation.

"Mphm!" he observed thoughtfully. "They
say that in a war every man has a bullet
waiting for him some place or other, with his
name on it! Sooner or later, he gets it. Aye!
Mphm!" He sucked his teeth reflectively, and
glanced towards the Field Ambulance. "Sooner
or later!"

"What for would he pit his name on it,
Wully?" inquired Nigg, who was not very
quick at grasping allusions.

"He wouldna pit on the name himself,"
explained the philosopher. "What I mean
is, there's a bullet for each one of us somewhere over there"—he jerked his head east-
wards—"in a Gairman pooch."

"What way could a Gairman pit my name
on a bullet?" demanded Nigg triumphantly.
"He doesna ken it!"

"Man," exclaimed Cosh, shedding some of
his philosophic calm, "can ye no unnerstand

that what I telled ye was jist a mainner of speakin'? When I said that a man's name was on a bullet, I didna mean that it was *written* there."

"Then what the hell *did* ye mean?" inquired the mystified disciple—not altogether unreasonably.

Private Tosh made a misguided but well-meaning attempt to straighten out the conversation.

"He means, Sandy," he explained in a soothing voice, "that the name was just stampit on the bullet. Like—like—like an identity disc!" he added brilliantly.

The philosopher clutched his temples with both hands.

"I dinna mean onything o' the kind," he roared. "What I intend tae imply is *this*, Sandy Nigg. Some place over there there is a bullet in a Gairman's pooch, and one day that bullet will find its way intil your insides as sure as if your name was written on it! *That's* what I meant. Jist a mainner of speakin'. Dae ye unnerstand me the noo?"

But it was the injured Buncle who replied —liked a lightning-flash.

"Never you fear, Sandy, boy!" he proclaimed to his perturbed ally. "That bullet has no' gotten your length yet. Maybe it never wull. There's mony a thing in this worrld with one man's name on it that finds its way intil the inside of some other man." He fixed Tosh with a relentless eye. "A bit ham, for instance!"

It was a knock-out blow.

"For ony sake," muttered the now demoralised Tosh, "drop the subject, and I'll gie ye a bit ham o' ma ain! There's just time tae cook it——"

"What kin' o' a fire is this?"

A cold shadow fell upon the group as a substantial presence inserted itself between the debaters and the wintry sunshine. Corporal Mucklewame was speaking, in his new and awful official voice, pointing an accusing finger at the fire, which, neglected in the ardour of discussion, was smoking furiously.

"Did you wish the hale wood tae be shelled?" continued Mucklewame sarcastically. "Put oot the fire at once, or I'll need tae bring ye all before the Officer. It is a cauld dinner ye'll get, and ye'll deserve it!"

## IV.

In the fire-trench—or perhaps it would be more correct to call it the water-trench—life may be short, and is seldom merry; but it is not often dull. For one thing, we are never idle.

A Boche trench-mortar knocks down several yards of your parapet. Straightway your machine-gunners are called up, to cover the gap until darkness falls and the gaping wound can be stanched with fresh sandbags. A mine has been exploded upon your front, leaving a crater into which predatory Boches will certainly creep at night. You summon a *posse* of bombers to occupy the cavity and discourage any such enterprise. The heavens open, and there is a sudden deluge. Immediately it is a case of all hands to the trench-pumps! A better plan, if you have the advantage of ground, is to cut a culvert under the parapet and pass the inundation on to a more deserving quarter. In any case you need never lack healthful exercise.

While upon the subject of mines, we may

note that this branch of military industry
has expanded of late to most unpleasant
dimensions. The Boche began it, of course
—he always initiates these undesirable pas-
times,—and now we have followed his lead
and caught him up.

To the ordinary mortal, to become a blind
groper amid the dark places of the earth, in
search of a foe whom it is almost certain death
to encounter there, seems perhaps the most
idiotic of all the idiotic careers open to those
who are idiotic enough to engage in modern
warfare. However, many of us are as much
at home below ground as above it. In more
peaceful times we were accustomed to spend
eight hours a day there, lying up against the
"face" in a tunnel perhaps four feet high, and
wielding a pick in an attitude which would
have convulsed any ordinary man with cramp.
But there are few ordinary men in "K (1)."
There is never any difficulty in obtaining
volunteers for the Tunnelling Company.

So far as the amateur can penetrate its
mysteries, mining, viewed under our present
heading—namely, Winter Sports—offers the
following advantages to its participants :—

(1) In winter it is much warmer below the earth than upon its surface, and Thomas Atkins is the most confirmed "frowster" in the world.

(2) Critics seldom descend into mines.

(3) There is extra pay.

The disadvantages are so obvious that they need not be enumerated here.

In these trenches we have been engaged upon a very pretty game of subterranean chess for some weeks past, and we are very much on our mettle. We have some small leeway to make up. When we took over these trenches, a German mine, which had been maturing (apparently unheeded) during the tenancy of our predecessors, was exploded two days after our arrival, inflicting heavy casualties upon "D" Company. Curiously enough, the damage to the trench was comparatively slight; but the tremendous shock of the explosion killed more than one man by concussion, and brought down the roofs of several dug-outs upon their sleeping occupants. Altogether it was a sad business, and the Battalion swore to be avenged.

So they called upon Lieutenant Duff-Bertram—usually called Bertie the Badger, in reference to his rodent disposition—to make the first move in the return match. Bertie and his troglodyte assistants accordingly sank a shaft in a retired spot of their own selecting, and proceeded to burrow forward towards the Boche lines.

After certain days Bertie presented himself, covered in clay, before Colonel Kemp, and made a report.

Colonel Kemp considered.

"You say you can hear the enemy working?" he said.

"Yes, sir."

"Near?"

"Pretty near, sir."

"How near?"

"A few yards."

"What do you propose to do?"

Bertie the Badger—in private life he was a consulting mining engineer with a beautiful office in Victoria Street and a nice taste in spats—scratched an earthy nose with a muddy forefinger.

"I think they are making a defensive gallery, sir," he announced.

"Let us have your statement in the simplest possible language, please," said Colonel

F

Kemp. "Some of my younger officers," he added rather ingeniously, "are not very expert in these matters."

Bertie the Badger thereupon expounded the situation with solemn relish. By a defensive gallery, it appeared that he meant a lateral tunnel running parallel with the trench line, in such a manner as to intercept any tunnel pushed out by the British miners.

"And what do you suggest doing to this Piccadilly Tube of theirs?" inquired the Colonel.

"I could dig forward and break into it, sir," suggested Bertie.

"That seems a move in the right direction," said the Colonel. "But won't the Boche try to prevent you?"

"Yes, sir."

"How?"

"He will wait until the head of my tunnel gets near enough, and then blow it in."

"That would be very tiresome of him. What other alternatives are open to you?"

"I could get as near as possible, sir," replied Bertie calmly, "and then blow up *his* gallery."

"That sounds better. Well, exercise your

own discretion, and don't get blown up unless you particularly want to. And above all, be quite sure that while you are amusing yourself with the Piccadilly Tube, the wily Boche isn't burrowing past *you*, and under my parapet, by the Bakerloo! Good luck! Report any fresh development at once."

So Bertie the Badger returned once more to his native element and proceeded to exercise his discretion. This took the form of continuing his aggressive tunnel in the direction of the Boche defensive gallery. Next morning, encouraged by the absolute silence of the enemy's miners, he made a farther and final push, which actually landed him in the "Piccadilly Tube" itself.

"This is a rum go, Howie!" he observed in a low voice to his corporal. "A long, beautiful gallery, five by four, lined with wood, electrically lighted, with every modern convenience—and not a Boche in it!"

"Varra bad discipline, sir!" replied Corporal Howie severely.

"Are you sure it isn't a trap?"

"It may be, sirr; but I doot the oversman is awa' to his dinner, and the men are back in the shaft, doing naething." Corporal Howie had been an "oversman" himself, and knew something of subterranean labour problems.

"Well, if you are right, the Boche must be getting demoralised. It is not like him to present us with openings like this. However, the first thing to do is to distribute a few souvenirs along the gallery. Pass the word back for the stuff. Meanwhile I shall endeavour to test your theory about the oversman's dinner-hour. I am going to creep along and have a look at the Boche entrance to the Tube. It's down there, at the south end of his gallery, I think. I can see a break in the wood lining. If you hear any shooting, you will know that the dinner-hour is over!"

At the end of half an hour the Piccadilly Tube was lined with sufficient explosive material to ensure the permanent closing of the line. Still no Boche had been seen or heard.

"Now, Howie," said Bertie the Badger, fingering the fuse, "what about it?"

"About what, sirr?" inquired Howie, who was not quite *au fait* with current catch-phrases.

"Are we going to touch off all this stuff

now, and clear out, or are we going to wait
and see?"

"I would like fine——" began the Corporal
wistfully.

"So would I," said Bertie. "Tell the men
to get back and out; and you and I will hold
on until the guests return from the banquet."

"Varra good, sirr."

For another half-hour the pair waited—
Bertie the Badger like a dog in its kennel,
with his head protruding into the hostile
gallery, while his faithful henchman crouched
close behind him. Deathly stillness reigned,
relieved only by an occasional thud, as a shell
or trench-mortar bomb exploded upon the
ground far above their heads.

"I'm going to have another look round
that corner," said Bertie at last. "Hold on
to the fuse."

He handed the end of the fuse to his subordinate, and having wormed his way out of
the tunnel, proceeded cautiously on all-fours
along the gallery. On his way he passed the
electric light. He twisted off the bulb and
crawled on in the dark.

Feeling his way by the east wall of the
gallery, he came presently to the break in

the woodwork. Very slowly, lying flat on his stomach now, he wriggled forward until his head came opposite the opening. A low passage ran away to his left, obviously leading back to the Boche trenches. Three yards from the entrance the passage bent sharply to the right, thus interrupting the line of sight.

"There's a light burning just round that bend," said Bertie the Badger to himself. "I wonder if it would be rash to go on and have a look at it!"

He was still straining at this gnat, when suddenly his elbow encountered a shovel which was leaning against the wall of the gallery. It tumbled down with a clatter almost stunning. Next moment a hand came round the bend of the tunnel and fired a revolver almost into the explorer's face.

Another shot rang out directly after.

The devoted Howie, hastening to the rescue, collided sharply with a solid body crawling towards him in the darkness.

"Curse you, Howie!" said the voice of Bertie the Badger, with refreshing earnestness. "Get back out of this. Where's your fuse?"

The pair scrambled back into their own tunnel, and the end of the fuse was soon recovered. Almost simultaneously three more revolver-shots ran out.

"I thought I had fixed that Boche," murmured Bertie in a disappointed voice. "I heard him grunt when my bullet hit him. Perhaps this is another one — or several. Keep back in the tunnel, Howie, confound you, and don't breathe up my sleeve! They are firing straight along the gallery now. I will return the compliment. Ouch!"

"What's the matter, sirr?" inquired the anxious voice of Howie, as his officer, who had tried to fire round the corner with his left hand, gave a sudden exclamation and rolled over upon his side.

"I must have been hit the first time," he explained. "Collar-bone, I think. I didn't know till I rested my weight on my left elbow. . . . Howie, I am going to exercise my discretion again. Somebody in this gallery is going to be blown up presently, and if you and I don't get a move on, p.d.q., it will be us! Give me the fuse-lighter, and wait for me at the foot of the shaft. Quick!"

Very reluctantly the Corporal obeyed.

However, he was in due course joined at the foot of the shaft by Bertie the Badger, groaning profanely; and the pair made their way to the upper regions with all possible speed. After a short interval, a sudden rumbling, followed by a heavy explosion, announced that the fuse had done its work, and that the Piccadilly Tube, the fruit of many toilsome weeks of Boche calculation and labour, had been permanently closed to traffic of all descriptions.

Bertie the Badger received a Military Cross, and his abettor the D.C.M.

## v.

But the newest and most fashionable form of winter sport this season is The Flying Matinée.

This entertainment takes place during the small hours of the morning, and is strictly limited to a duration of ten minutes—quite long enough for most *matinées*, too. The actors are furnished by a unit of " K (1) " and the *rôle* of audience is assigned to the inhabitants of the Boche trenches immediately

opposite. These matinées have proved an
enormous success, but require most careful
rehearsal.

It is two A.M., and comparative peace reigns
up and down the line. The rain of star-shells,
always prodigal in the early evening, has died
down to a mere drizzle. Working and fatigue
parties, which have been busy since darkness
set in at five o'clock,—rebuilding parapets,
repairing wire, carrying up rations, and patrol-
ling debatable areas, — have ceased their
labours, and are sleeping heavily until the
coming of the wintry dawn shall rouse them,
grimy and shivering, to another day's unpleasantness.

Private Hans Dumpkopf, on sentry duty in
the Boche firing trench, gazes mechanically
over the parapet ; but the night is so dark and
the wind so high that it is difficult to see and
quite impossible to hear anything. He shelters
himself beside a traverse, and waits patiently
for his relief. It begins to rain, and Hans,
after cautiously reconnoitring the other side
of the traverse, to guard against prowling
sergeants, sidles a few yards to his right
beneath the friendly cover of an improvised
roof of corrugated iron sheeting, laid across

the trench from parapet to parados. It is quite dry here, and comparatively warm. Hans closes his eyes for a moment, and heaves a gentle sigh.

Next moment there comes a rush of feet in the darkness, followed by a metallic clang, as of hobnailed boots on metal. Hans, lying prostrate and half-stunned beneath the galvanised iron sheeting, which, dislodged from its former position by the impact of a heavy body descending from above, now forms part of the flooring of the trench, is suddenly aware that this same trench is full of men—rough, uncultured men, clad in short petticoats and the skins of wild animals, and armed with knobkerries. The Flying Matinée has begun, and Hans Dumpkopf has got in by the early door.

Each of the performers—there are fifty of them all told—has his part to play, and plays it with commendable aplomb. One, having disarmed an unresisting prisoner, assists him over the parapet and escorts him affectionately to his new home. Another clubs a recalcitrant foeman over the head with a knobkerry, and having thus reduced him to a more amenable frame of mind, hoists him over the parapet and drags him after his " kamerad."

Other parties are told off to deal with the
dug-outs. As a rule, the occupants of these
are too dazed to make any resistance,—to be
quite frank, the individual Boche in these
days seems rather to welcome captivity than
otherwise,—and presently more of the "bag"
are on their way to the British lines.

But by this time the performance is drawing to a close. The alarm has been communicated to the adjacent sections of the trench,
and preparations for the ejection of the in-
truders are being hurried forward. That is
to say, German bombers are collecting upon
either flank, with the intention of bombing
"inwards" until the impudent foe has been
destroyed or evicted. As we are not here to
precipitate a general action, but merely to
round up a few prisoners and do as much
damage as possible in ten minutes, we hasten
to the *finale*. As in most *finales*, one's ac-
tions now become less restrained—but, from
a brutal point of view, more effective. A
couple of hand-grenades are thrown into any
dug-out which has not yet surrendered.
(The Canadians, who make quite a speciality
of flying *matinées*, are accustomed, we understand, as an artistic variant to this practice,

to fasten an electric torch along the barrel of
a rifle, and so illuminate their lurking targets
while they shoot.) A sharp order passes
along the line; every one scrambles out of
the trench; and the troupe makes its way
back, before the enemy in the adjacent
trenches have really wakened up, to the
place from which it came. The *matinée*, so
far as the actors are concerned, is over.

Not so the audience. The avenging host
is just getting busy. The bombing parties
are now marshalled, and proceed with awful
solemnity and Teutonic thoroughness to clear
the violated trench. The procedure of a
bombing party is stereotyped. They begin
by lobbing hand-grenades over the first
traverse into the first bay. After the
ensuing explosion, they trot round the
traverse in single file and occupy the bay.
This manœuvre is then repeated until the
entire trench is cleared. The whole operation
requires good discipline, considerable courage,
and carefully timed co-operation with the
other bombing party. In all these attributes
the Boche excels. But one thing is essential
to the complete success of his efforts, and that

is the presence of the enemy. When, after methodically desolating each bay in turn (and incidentally killing their own wounded in the process), the two parties meet midway—practically on top of the unfortunate Hans Dumpkopf, who is still giving an imitation of a tortoise in a corrugated shell—it is discovered that the beautifully executed counter-attack has achieved nothing but the recapture of an entirely empty trench. The birds have flown, taking their prey with them. Hans is the sole survivor, and after hearing what his officer has to say to him upon the subject, bitterly regrets the fact.

Meanwhile, in the British trenches a few yards away, the box-office returns are being made up. These take the form, firstly, of some fourteen prisoners, including one indignant officer—he had been pulled from his dug-out half asleep and frog-marched across the British lines by two private soldiers well qualified to appreciate the richness of his language — together with various souvenirs in the way of arms and accoutrements; and secondly, of the knowledge that at least as many more of the enemy had been left permanently incapacitated for further warfare in the dug-outs. A grim and grisly drama when you come to criticise it in cold blood, but not without a certain humour of its own — and most demoralising for Brother Boche!

But he is a slow pupil. He regards the profession of arms and the pursuit of war with such intense and solemn reverence that he *cannot* conceive how any one calling himself a soldier can be so criminally frivolous as to write a farce round the subject—much less present the farce at a Flying *Matinée*. That possibly explains why the following stately paragraph appeared a few days later in the periodical *communiqué* which keeps the German nation in touch with its Army's latest exploits :—

*During the night of Dec. 4th-5th attempts were made by strong detachments of the enemy to penetrate our line near Sloozleschump, S.E. of Ypres. The attack failed utterly.*

"And they don't even realise that it was only a leg-pull!" commented the Company

Commander who had stage-managed the affair. "These people simply don't deserve to have entertainments arranged for them at all. Well, we must pull the limb again, that's all!"

And it was so.

# CHAPTER FOUR.

## THE PUSH THAT FAILED.

"I WONDER if they really mean business this time," surmised that youthful Company Commander, Temporary Captain Bobby Little, to Major Wagstaffe.

"It sounds like it," said Wagstaffe, as another salvo of "whizz-bangs" broke like inflammatory surf upon the front-line trenches. "Intermittent strafes we are used to, but this all-day performance seems to indicate that the Boche is really getting down to it for once. The whole proceeding reminds me of nothing so much as our own 'artillery preparation' before the big push at Loos."

"Then you think the Boches are going to make a push of their own?"

"I do; and I hope it will be a good fat one. When it comes, I fancy we shall be

able to put up something rather pretty in the
way of a defence.  The Salient is stiff with
guns—I don't think the Boche quite realises
how stiff!  And we owe the swine something!" he added through his teeth.

There was a pause in the conversation.
You cannot hold the Salient for three months
without paying for the distinction ; and the
regiment had paid its full share.  Not so
much in numbers, perhaps, as in quality.
Stray bullets, whistling up and down the
trenches, coming even obliquely from the rear,
had exacted most grievous toll.  Shells and
trench-mortar bombs, taking us in flank, had
extinguished many valuable lives.  At this
time nothing but the best seemed to satisfy
the fates.  One day it would be a trusted
colour-sergeant, on another a couple of particularly promising young corporals.  Only last
week the Adjutant—athlete, scholar, born
soldier, and very lovable schoolboy, all most
perfectly blended — had fallen mortally
wounded, on his morning round of the fire-
trenches, by a bullet which came from no-
where.  He was the subject of Wagstaffe's
reference.

" Is it not possible," suggested Mr Waddell,

G

who habitually considered all questions from every possible point of view, "that this bombardment has been specially initiated by the German authorities, in order to impress upon their own troops a warning that there must be no Christmas truce this year?"

"If that is the Kaiser's Christmas greeting to his loving followers," observed Wagstaffe dryly, "I think he might safely have left it to us to deliver it!"

"They say," interposed Bobby Little, "that the Kaiser is here himself."

"How do you know?"

"It was rumoured in *Comic Cuts*." (*Comic Cuts* is the stately Summary of War Intelligence issued daily from Olympus.)

"If that is true," said Wagstaffe, "they probably will attack. All this fuss and bobbery suggest something of the kind. They remind me of the commotion which used to precede Arthur Roberts's entrance in the old days of Gaiety burlesque. Before your time, I fancy, Bobby?"

"Yes," said Bobby modestly. "I first found touch with the Gaiety over *Our Miss Gibbs*. And I was quite a kid even then," he added, with characteristic honesty. " But what about Arthur Roberts ? "

" Some forty or fifty years ago," explained Wagstaffe, " when I was in the habit of frequenting places of amusement, Arthur Roberts was leading man at the establishment to which I have referred. He usually came on about half-past eight, just as the show was beginning to lose its first wind. His entrance was a most tremendous affair. First of all the entire chorus blew in from the wings—about sixty of them in ten seconds—saying ' Hurrah, hurrah, girls ! ' or something rather unusual of that kind ; after which minor characters rushed on from opposite sides and told one another that Arthur Roberts was coming. Then the band played, and everybody began to tell the audience about it in song. When everything was in full blast, the great man would appear—stepping out of a bathing-machine, or falling out of a hansom-cab, or sliding down a chute on a toboggan. He was assisted to his feet by the chorus, and then proceeded to ginger the show up. Well, that's how this present entertainment impresses me. All this noise and obstreperousness are leading up to one thing—Kaiser

Bill's entrance. Preliminary bombardment—
that's the chorus getting to work! Minor
characters— the trench-mortars—spread the
glad news! Band *and* chorus—that's the
grand attack working up to boiling - point!
Finally, preceded by clouds of gas, the Arch-
Comedian in person, supported by spectacled
*coryphées* in brass hats! How's that for a
Christmas pantomime?"

"Rotten!" said Bobby, as a shell sang
over the parapet and burst in the wood
behind.

## II.

Kaiser or no Kaiser, Major Wagstaffe's extravagant analogy held good. As Christmas
drew nearer, the band played louder and
faster; the chorus swelled higher and shriller,
and it became finally apparent that something (or somebody) of portentous importance
was directing the storm.

Between six and seven next morning, the
Battalion, which had stood to arms all night,
lifted up its heavy head and sniffed the misty
dawn-wind—an east wind—dubiously. Next
moment gongs were clanging up and down the

trench, and men were tearing open the satchels which contained their anti-gas helmets.

Major Wagstaffe, who had been sent up from Battalion Headquarters to take general charge of affairs in the firing trench, buttoned the bottom edge of his helmet well inside his collar and clambered up on the firing-step to take stock of the position. He crouched low, for a terrific bombardment was in progress, and shells were almost grazing the parapet.

Presently he was joined by a slim young officer similarly disguised. It was the Commander of "A" Company. Wagstaffe placed his head close to Bobby's left ear, and shouted through the cloth—

"We shan't feel this gas much. They're letting it off higher up the line. Look!"

Bobby, laboriously inhaling the tainted air inside his helmet,—being preserved from a gas attack is only one degree less unpleasant than being gassed,—turned his goggles northward.

In the dim light of the breaking day he could discern a greenish-yellow cloud rolling across from the Boche trenches on his left.

"Will they attack?" he bellowed.

Wagstaffe nodded his head, and then

cautiously unbuttoned his collar and rolled up the front of his helmet. Then, after delicately sampling the atmosphere by a cautious sniff, he removed his helmet altogether. Bobby followed his example. The air was not by any means so pure as might have been desired, but it was infinitely preferable to that inside a gas-helmet.

"Nothing to signify," pronounced Wagstaffe. "We're only getting the edge of it. Sergeant, pass down that men may roll up their helmets, but must keep them on their heads. Now, Bobby, things are getting interesting. Will they attack, or will they not?"

"What do you think?" asked Bobby.

"They are certainly going to attack farther north. The Boche does not waste gas as a rule—not this sort of gas! And I think he'll attack here too. The only reason why he has not switched on our anæsthetic is that the wind isn't quite right for this bit of the line. I think it is going to be a general push. Bobby, have a look through this sniper's loophole. Can you see any bayonets twinkling in the Boche trenches?"

Bobby applied an eye to the loophole.

"Yes," he said, "I can see them. Those trenches must be packed with men."

"Absolutely stiff with them," agreed Wagstaffe, getting out his revolver. "We shall be in for it presently. Are your fellows all ready, Bobby?"

The youthful Captain ran his eye along the trench, where his Company, with magazines loaded and bayonets fixed, were grimly awaiting the onset. There had been an onset similar to this, with the same green, nauseous accompaniment, in precisely the same spot eight months before, which had broken the line and penetrated for four miles. There it had been stayed by a forlorn hope—gasping, choking, but indomitable—and disaster had been most gloriously retrieved. What was going to happen this time? One thing was certain: the day of stink-pots was over.

"When do you think they'll attack?" shouted Bobby to Wagstaffe, battling against the noise of bursting shells.

"Quite soon—in a minute or two. Their guns will stop directly—to lift their sights and set up a barrage behind us. Then,

perhaps, the Boche will step over his parapet.
Perhaps not!"

The last sentence rang out with uncanny
distinctness, for the German guns with one
accord had ceased firing. For a full two
minutes there was absolute silence, while the
bayonets in the opposite trenches twinkled
with tenfold intent.

Then, from every point in the great Salient
of Ypres, the British guns replied.

Possibly the Great General Staff at Berlin
had been misinformed as to the exact strength
of the British Artillery. Possibly they had
been informed by their Intelligence Department that Trades Unionism had ensured that
a thoroughly inadequate supply of shells was
to hand in the Salient. Or possibly they had
merely decided, after the playful habit of
General Staffs, to let the infantry in the
trenches take their chance of any retaliation
that might be forthcoming.

Whatever these great men were expecting,
it is highly improbable that they expected
that which arrived. Suddenly the British
batteries spoke out, and they all spoke
together. In the space of four minutes they

deposited *thirty thousand* high-explosive shells
in the Boche front-line trenches—yea, distri-
buted the same accurately and evenly along
all that crowded arc. Then they paused, as
suddenly as they began, while British rifle-
men and machine - gunners bent to their
work.

But few received the order to fire. Here
and there a wave of men broke over the German parapet and rolled towards the British
lines—only to be rolled back crumpled up
by machine-guns. Never once was the goal
reached. The great Christmas attack was
over. After months of weary waiting and
foolish recrimination, that exasperating race
of bad starters but great stayers, the British
people, had delivered " the goods," and made
it possible for their soldiers to speak with the
enemy in the gate upon equal—nay, superior,
terms.

" Is that all ? " asked Bobby Little, peering
out over the parapet, a little awestruck at the
devastation over the way.

" That is all," said Wagstaffe, " or I'm a
Boche ! There will be much noise and some
irregular scrapping for days, but the tin lid

has been placed upon the grand attack.    The
great Christmas Victory is off!"

Then he added, thoughtfully, referring apparently to the star performer—

"We *have* been and spoiled his entrance for
him, haven't we?"

# CHAPTER FIVE.

## UNBENDING THE BOW.

THERE is a certain kind of English country-house female who is said to "live in her boxes." That is to say, she appears to possess no home of her own, but flits from one indulgent roof-tree to another; and owing to the fact that she is invariably put into a bedroom whose wardrobe is full of her hostess' superannuated ball-frocks and winter furs, never knows what it is to have all her "things" unpacked at once.

Well, we out here cannot be said to live in our boxes, for we do not possess any; but we do most undoubtedly live in our haversacks and packs. And this brings us to the matter in hand—namely, so-called Rest-Billets. The whole of the *hinterland* of this great trench

line is full of tired men, seeking for a place to
lie down in, and living in their boxes when
they find one.

At present we are indulging in such a
period of repose ; and we venture to think
that on the whole we have earned it.  Our
last rest was in high summer, when we lay
about under an August sun in the district
round Bethune, and called down curses upon
all flying and creeping insects.  Since then
we have undergone certain so-called "operations" in the neighbourhood of Loos, and have
put in three months in the Salient of Ypres.
As that devout adherent of the Roman faith,
Private Reilly, of "B" Company, put it to
his spiritual adviser—

"I doot we'll get excused a good slice of
Purgatory for this, father !"

We came out of the Salient just before Christmas, in the midst of the mutual unpleasantness arising out of the grand attack upon the
British line which was to have done so much to
restore the waning confidence of the Hun.  It
was meant to be a big affair—a most majestic
victory, in fact; but our new gas-helmets
nullified the gas, and our new shells paralysed
the attack ; so the Third Battle of Ypres was

not yet. Still, as I say, there was considerable unpleasantness all round; and we were escorted upon our homeward way, from Sanctuary Wood to Zillebeke, and from Zillebeke to Dickebusche, by a swarm of angry and disappointed shells.

Next day we found ourselves many miles behind the firing line, once more in France, with a whole month's holiday in prospect, comfortably conscious that one could walk round a corner or look over a wall without preliminary reconnaissance or subsequent extirpation.

As for the holiday itself, unreasonable persons are not lacking to point out that it is of the 'busman's variety. It is true that we are no longer face to face with the foe, but we—or rather, the authorities—make believe that we are. We wage mimic warfare in full marching order; we fire rifles and machine-guns upon improvised ranges; we perform hazardous feats with bombs and a dummy trench. More galling still, we are back in the region of squad-drill, physical exercises, and handling of arms—horrors of our childhood which we thought had been left safely interned at Aldershot.

But the authorities are wise. The regiment
is stiff and out of condition : it is suffering from moral and intellectual " trench-feet."
Heavy drafts have introduced a large and un-
tempered element into our composition. Many
of the subalterns are obviously " new-jined "
—as the shrewd old lady of Ayr once observed
of the rubicund gentleman at the temperance
meeting. Their men hardly knew them or
one another by sight. The regiment must
be moulded anew, and its lustre restored by
the beneficent process vulgarly know as " spit
and polish." So every morning we apply
ourselves with thoroughness, if not enthusiasm, to tasks which remind us of last winter's
training upon the Hampshire chalk.

But the afternoon and evening are a different story altogether. If we were busy in
the morning, we are busier still for the rest of
the day. There is football galore, for we
have to get through a complete series of
Divisional cup-ties in four weeks. There is
also a Brigade boxing tournament. (No, that
was not where Private Tosh got his black
eye : that is a souvenir of New Year's Eve.)
There are entertainments of various kinds in
the recreation-tent. This whistling platoon,

with towels round their necks, are on their
way to the nearest convent, or asylum, or
École des Jeunes Filles—have no fear; these
establishments are untenanted!—for a bath.
There, in addition to the pleasures of ablution, they will receive a partial change of
raiment.

Other signs of regeneration are visible.
That mysterious-looking vehicle, rather re-
sembling one of the early locomotives exhibited in the South Kensington Museum,
standing in the mud outside a farm-billet,
with its superheated interior stuffed with
"C" Company's blankets, is performing an
unmentionable but beneficent work.

Buttons are resuming their polish; the
pattern of our kilts is emerging from its
superficial crust; and Church Parade is once
more becoming quite a show affair.

Away to the east the guns still thunder,
and at night the star-shells float tremblingly
up over the distant horizon. But not for us.
Not yet, that is. In a few weeks' time we
shall be back in another part of the line. Till
then—Company drill and Cup Ties! *Carpe
diem!*

## II.

It all seemed very strange and unreal to
Second-Lieutenant Angus M‘Lachlan, as he
alighted from the train at railhead, and supervised the efforts of his solitary N.C.O. to
arrange the members of his draft in a straight
line. There were some thirty of them in all.
Some were old hands — men from the First
and Second Battalions, who had been home
wounded, and had now been sent out to leaven
" K (1)." Others were Special Reservists
from the Third Battalion. These had been at
the Depôt for a long time, and some of them
stood badly in need of a little active service.
Others, again, were new hands altogether—
the product of " K to the $n^{\text{th}}$." Among these
Angus M‘Lachlan numbered himself, and he
made no attempt to conceal the fact. The
novelty of the sights around him was almost
too much for his dignity as a commissioned
officer.

Angus M‘Lachlan was a son of the Manse,
and incidentally a child of Nature. The
Manse was a Highland Manse ; and until a
few months ago Angus had never, save for a

rare visit to distant Edinburgh, penetrated
beyond the small town which lay four miles
from his native glen, and of whose local
Academy he had been "dux." When the
War broke out he had been upon the point of
proceeding to Edinburgh University, where
he had already laid siege to a bursary, and
captured the same; but all these plans, together with the plans of countless more distinguished persons, had been swept to the
winds by the invasion of Belgium. On that
date Angus summoned up his entire stock of
physical and moral courage and informed his
reverend parent of his intention to enlist for a
soldier. Permission was granted with quite
stunning readiness. Neil M'Lachlan believed
in straight hitting both in theology and war,
and was by no means displeased at the martial
aspirations of his only son. If he quitted
himself like a man in the forefront of battle,
the boy could safely look forward to being
cock of his own Kirk-Session in the years that
came afterwards. One reservation the old
man made. His son, as a Highland gentleman, would lead men to battle, and not merely
accompany them. So the impatient Angus
was bidden to apply for a Commission—his

H

attention during the period of waiting being
directed by his parent to the study of the
campaigns of Joshua, and the methods employed by that singular but successful strategist in dealing with the Philistine.

Angus had a long while to wait, for all the
youth of England—and Scotland too—was
on fire, and others nearer the fountain of
honour had to be served first.  But his turn
came at last; and we now behold him, as
typical a product of K to the $n^{th}$ as Bobby
Little had been of K (1), standing at last upon
the soil of France, and inquiring in a soft
Highland voice for the Headquarters of our
own particular Battalion.

He had half expected, half hoped, to alight
from the train amidst a shower of shells, as
he knew the Old Regiment had done many
months before, just after the War broke out.
But all he saw upon his arrival was an untidy
goods yard, littered with military stores, and
peopled by British privates in the *déshabille*
affected by the British Army when engaged
in menial tasks.

Being quite ignorant of the whereabouts of
his regiment—when last heard of they had
been in trenches near Ypres—and failing to

recollect the existence of that autocratic but indispensable *genius loci*, the R.T.O., Angus took uneasy stock of his surroundings and wondered what to do next.

Suddenly a friendly voice at his elbow remarked—

"There's a queer lot o' bodies hereaboot, sirr."

Angus turned, to find that he was being addressed by a short, stout private of the draft, in a kilt much too big for him.

"Indeed that is so," he replied politely. "What is your name?"

"Peter Bogle, sirr. I am frae oot of Kirkintilloch." Evidently gratified by the success of his conversational opening, the little man continued—

"I would like fine for tae get a contrack oot here after the War. This country is in a terrible state o' disrepair." Then he added confidentially—

"I'm a hoose-painter tae a trade."

"I should not like to be that myself," replied Angus, whose early training as a minister's son was always causing him to forget the social gulf which is fixed between officers and the rank-and-file. "Climbing ladders makes me dizzy."

"Och, it's naething! A body gets used tae it," Mr Bogle assured him.

Angus was about to proceed further with the discussion, when the cold and disapproving voice of the draft-sergeant announced in his ear—

"An officer wishes to speak to you, sir."

Second - Lieutenant M'Lachlan, suddenly awake to the enormity of his conduct, turned guiltily to greet the officer, while the sergeant abruptly hunted the genial Private Bogle back into the ranks.

Angus found himself confronted by an immaculate young gentleman wearing two stars. Angus, who only wore one, saluted hurriedly.

"Morning," observed the stranger. "You in charge of this draft?"

"Yes, sir," said Angus respectfully.

"Righto! You are to march them to "A" Company billets. I'll show you the way. My name's Cockerell. Your train is late. What time did you leave the Base?"

"Indeed," replied Angus meekly, "I am not quite sure. We had barely landed when they told me the train would start at seventeen-forty. What time would that be—sir?"

"About a quarter to six: more likely about

midnight! Well, get your bunch on to the
road, and—Hallo, what's the matter? Let
go!"

The new officer was gripping him excitedly
by the arm, and as the new officer stood six-
foot - four, and was brawny in proportion,
Master Cockerell's appeal was uttered in a
tone of unusual sincerity.

"Look!" cried Angus excitedly. "The
dogs, the dogs!"

A small cart was passing swiftly by, towed
by two sturdy hounds of unknown degree.
They were pulling with the feverish enthusiasm which distinguishes the Dog in
the service of Man, and were being urged
to further efforts by a small hatless girl
carrying the inevitable large umbrella.

"All right!" exclaimed Cockerell curtly.
"Custom of the country, and all that."

The impulsive Angus apologised; and the
draft, having been safely manœuvred on to the
road, formed fours and set out upon its march.

"Are the battalion in the trenches at
present, sir?" inquired Angus.

"No. Rest - billets two miles from here.
About time, too! You'll get lots of work
to do, though."

"I shall welcome that," said Angus simply. "In the depôt at home we were terribly idle. There is a windmill!"

"Yes; one sees them occasionally out here," replied Cockerell drily.

"Everything is so strange!" confessed the open-hearted Angus. "Those dogs we saw just now—the people with their sabots—the country carts, like wheelbarrows with three wheels—the little shrines at the cross-roads—the very children talking French so glibly——"

"Wonderful how they pick it up!" agreed Cockerell. But the sarcasm was lost on his companion, whose attention was now riveted upon an approaching body of infantry, about fifty strong.

"What troops are those, please?"

Cockerell knitted his brows sardonically.

"It's rather hard to tell at this distance," he said; "but I rather think they are the Grenadier Guards."

Two minutes later the procession had been met and passed. It consisted entirely of elderly gentlemen in ill-fitting khaki, clumping along upon their flat feet and smoking clay pipes. They carried shovels on their shoulders, and made not the slightest response when called upon by the soldierly old corporal who led them to give Mr Cockerell "eyes left!" On the contrary, engaged as they were in heated controversy or amiable conversation with one another, they cut him dead.

Angus M'Lachlan said nothing for quite five minutes. Then—

"I suppose," he said almost timidly, "that those were members of a *Reserve* Regiment of the Guards?"

Cockerell, who had never outgrown certain characteristics which most of us shed upon emerging from the Lower Fourth, laughed long and loud.

"That crowd? They belong to one of the Labour Battalions. They make roads, and dig support-trenches, and sling mud about generally. Wonderful old sportsmen! Pleased as Punch when a shell falls within half a mile of them. Something to write home about. What? I say, I pulled your leg that time! Here we are at Headquarters. Come and report to the C.O. Grenadier Guards! My aunt!"

Angus, although his Celtic enthusiasm sometimes led him into traps, was no fool. He soon settled down in his new surroundings, and found favour with Colonel Kemp, which was no light achievement.

"You won't find that the War, in its present stage, calls for any display of genius," the Colonel explained to Angus at their first interview. "I don't expect my officers to exhibit any quality but the avoidance of *sloppiness*. If I detail you to be at a certain spot, at a certain hour, with a certain number of men — a ration-party, or a working-party, or a burial-party, or anything you like, — all I ask is that you will be *there*, at the appointed hour, with the whole of your following. That may not sound a very difficult feat, but experience has taught me that if a man can achieve it, and can be *relied* upon to achieve it under present conditions, say, nine times out of ten—well, he is a pearl of price; and there is not a C.O. in the British Army who wouldn't scramble to get him. That's all, M'Lachlan. Good morning!"

By punctilious attention to this sound advice Angus soon began to build up a reputation. He treated war - worn veterans like Bobby Little with immense respect, and this, too, was counted to him for righteousness. He exercised his platoon with appalling vigour. Upon Company route - marches he had to be embedded in some safe place in the middle of the column; in fact, his enormous stride and pedestrian enthusiasm would have reduced his followers to pulp. At Mess he was mute: like a wise man, he was feeling for his feet.

And being, like Moses, slow of tongue, he provided himself with an Aaron. Quite inadvertently, be it said. Bidden to obtain a servant for his personal needs, he selected the only man in the Battalion whose name he knew — Private Bogle, the *ci - devant* painter of houses. That friendly creature obeyed the call with alacrity. If his housepainting was no better than his valeting, then his prospects of a "contrack" after the War were poor indeed; but as a Mess-waiter he was a joy for ever. Despite the blood-curdling whispers of the Mess Corporal, his natural urbanity of disposition could not be stemmed. Of the comfort of others he was solicitous to the point of oppressiveness. A Mess-waiter's

idea of efficiency as a rule is to stand woodenly
at attention in an obscure corner of the room.
When called upon, he starts forward with a
jerk, and usually trips over something—probably his own feet.　Not so Private Bogle.

"Wull you try another cup o' tea, Major?"
he would suggest at breakfast to Major Wagstaffe, leaning affectionately over the back of
his chair.

"No, thank you, Bogle," Major Wagstaffe
would reply gravely.

"Weel, it's cauld onyway," Bogle would
rejoin, anxious to endorse his superior's
decision.

Or—in the same spirit—

"Wull I luft the soup now, sir?"

"*No!*"

"Varra weel: I'll jist let it bide the way
it is."

Lastly, Angus M'Lachlan proved himself a
useful acquisition—especially in rest-billets—
as an athlete.　He arrived just in time to
take part—no mean part, either—in a Rugby
Football match played between the officers of
two Brigades.　Thanks very largely to his
masterly leading of the forwards, our Brigade

were preserved from defeat at the hands of
their opponents, who on paper had appeared
to be irresistible.

Rugby Football "oot here" is a rarity,
though Association, being essentially the
game of the rank-and-file, flourishes in every
green field. But an Inverleith or Queen's
Club crowd would have recognised more than
one old friend among the thirty who took the
field that day. There were those participat-
ing whose last game had been one of the
spring "Internationals" in 1914, and who had
been engaged in a prolonged and strenuous
version of an even greater International ever
since August of that fateful year. Every
public school in Scotland was represented—
sometimes three or four times over — and
there were numerous doughty contributions
from establishments south of the Tweed.

The lookers-on were in different case. They
were to a man devoted—nay, frenzied—adher-
ents of the Association code. In less spaci-
ous days they had surged in their thousands
every Saturday afternoon to Ibrox, or Tyne-
castle, or Parkhead, there to yell themselves
into convulsions—now exhorting a friend to
hit some one a kick on the nose, now sternly

recommending the foe to play the game, now hoarsely consigning the referee to perdition. To these, Rugby Football—the greatest of all manly games—was a mere name. Their attitude when the officers appeared upon the field was one of indulgent superiority—the sort of superiority that a brawny pitman exhibits when his Platoon Commander steps down into a trench to lend a hand with the digging.

But in five minutes their mouths were agape with scandalised astonishment; in ten, the heavens were rent with their protesting cries. Accustomed to see football played with the feet, and to demand with one voice the instant execution of any player (on the other side) who laid so much as a finger upon the ball or the man who was playing it, the exhibition of savage and promiscuous brutality to which their superiors now treated them shocked the assembled spectators to the roots of their sensitive souls. Howls of virtuous indignation burst forth upon all sides.

When the three-quarter-backs brought off a brilliant passing run, there were stern cries of "Haands, there, referee!" When Bobby Little stopped an ugly rush by hurling himself

on the ball, the supporters of the other Brigade
greeted his heroic devotion with yells of exe-
cration.    When Angus M'Lachlan saved a
certain try by tackling a speedy wing three-
quarter low and bringing him down with a
crash, a hundred voices demanded his expul-
sion from the field.   And when Mr Waddell,
playing a stuffy but useful game at half,
gained fifty yards for his side by a series of
judicious little kicks into touch, the spectators
groaned aloud, and remarked caustically—

"This maun be a Cup-Tie, boys! They are
playin' for a draw, for tae get a second
gate!"

Altogether a thoroughly enjoyable afternoon, both for players and spectators.   And
so home to tea, domesticity, and social intercourse.   In this connection it may be noted
that our relations with the inhabitants are
of the friendliest.   On the stroke of six—
oh yes, we have our licensing restrictions out
here too!—half a dozen kilted warriors stroll
into the farm kitchen, and mumble affably to
Madame—

"Bone sworr!   Beer?"

France boasts one enormous advantage over
Scotland.   At home, you have at least to walk

to the corner of the street to obtain a drink :
"oot here" you can purchase beer in practically every house in a village. The French
licensing laws are a thing of mystery, but the
system appears roughly to be this. Either
you possess a licence, or you do not. If you
do, you may sell beer, and nothing else. If
you do not, you may—or at any rate do—sell
anything you like, including beer.

However, we have left our friends thirsty.
Their wants are supplied with cheerful
alacrity, and, having been accommodated with
seats round the stove, they converse with the
family. Heaven only knows what they talk
about, but talk they do—in the throaty unintelligible Doric of the Clydeside, with an
occasional Gallicism, like, "Allyman no bon !"
or "Compree?" thrown in as a sop to foreign
idiosyncracies. Madame and family respond,
chattering French (or Flemish) at enormous
speed. The amazing part of it all is that
neither side appears to experience the slightest
difficulty in understanding the other. One day
Mr Waddell, in the course of a friendly chat
with his hostess of the moment—she was
unable to speak a word of English—received
her warm congratulations upon his contem-

plated union with a certain fair one of St
Andrews. Mr Waddell, a very fair linguist,
replied in suitable but embarrassed terms,
and asked for the source of the good lady's
information.

" Mais votre ordonnance, m'sieur ! " was the
reply.

Tackled upon the subject, the " ordonnance "
in question, Waddell's servant — a shock-
headed youth from Dundee—admitted having
communicated the information ; and added—

" She's a decent body, sirr, the lady o' the
hoose. She lost her husband, she was tellin'
me, three years ago. She has twa sons in
the Airmy. Her auld Auntie is up at the
top o' the hoose—lyin' badly, and no expectin'
tae rise."

And yet some people study Esperanto !

We also make ourselves useful. " K (1) "
contains members of every craft. If the pig-
sty door is broken, a carpenter is forthcoming
to mend it. Somebody's elbow goes through
a pane of glass in the farm kitchen : straightway a glazier materialises from the nearest
platoon and puts in another. The ancestral
eight-day clock of the household develops in-
ternal complications, and is forthwith dismem-

bered and re-assembled, " with punctuality,
civility, and despatch," by a gentleman who,
until a few short months ago, had done nothing
else for fifteen years.

And it was in this connection that Corporal
Mucklewame stumbled on to a rare and congenial job, and incidentally made the one joke
of his life.

One afternoon a cow, the property of Madame
*la fermière*, developed symptoms of some
serious disorder. A period of dolorous bellow-
ing was followed by an outburst of homicidal
mania, during which " A" Company prudently
barricaded itself into the barn, the sufferer
having taken entire possession of the farmyard. Next, and finally—so rapidly did the
malady run its course—a state of coma intervened ; and finally the cow, collapsing
upon the doorstep of the Officers' Mess,
breathed her last before any one could be
found to point out to her the liberty she
was taking.

It was decided to hold a *post-mortem*—
firstly, to ascertain the cause of death ;
secondly, because it is easier to remove a dead
cow after dissection than before. Madame
therefore announced her intention of sending

for the butcher, and was on the point of doing
so when Corporal Mucklewame, in whose heart,
at the spectacle of the stark and lifeless
corpse, ancient and romantic memories were
stirring—it may be remembered that before
answering to the call of "K (1)" Mucklewame
had followed the calling of butcher's assistant
at Wishaw — volunteered for the job.    His
services were cordially accepted by thrifty
Madame ; and the Corporal, surrounded by a
silent and admiring crowd, set to work.

The officers, leaving the Junior Subaltern
in charge, went with one accord for a long
country walk.

Half an hour later Mucklewame arrived
at the seat of the deceased animal's trouble
—the seat of most of the troubles of man-
kind — its stomach.    After a brief investigation, he produced therefrom a small bag
of nails, recently missed from the vicinity of
a cook-house in course of construction in the
corner of the yard.

Abandoning the *rôle* of surgical expert for
that of coroner, Mucklewame held the trophy
aloft, and delivered his verdict—

"There, boys !   That's what comes of eating
your iron ration without authority !"

### III.

Here is an average billet, and its *personnel*.

The central feature of our residence is the refuse-pit, which fills practically the whole of the rectangular farmyard, and resembles (in size and shape *only*) an open-air swimming bath. Its abundant contents are apparently the sole asset of the household; for if you proceed, in the interests of health, to spread a decent mantle of honest earth thereover, you do so to the accompaniment of a harmonised chorus of lamentation, very creditably rendered by the entire family, who are grouped *en masse* about the spot where the high diving-board ought to be.

Round this perverted place of ablution runs a stone ledge, some four feet wide, and round that again run the farm buildings—the house at the top end, a great barn down one side, and the cowhouse, together with certain darksome piggeries and fowl-houses, down the other. These latter residences are only occupied at night, their tenants preferring to spend the golden hours of day in profitable occupation upon the happy hunting-ground in the middle.

Within the precincts of this already over-
crowded establishment are lodged some two
hundred British soldiers and their officers.
The men sleep in the barn, their meals being
prepared for them upon the Company cooker,
which stands in the muddy road outside, and
resembles the humble vehicle employed by
Urban District Councils for the preparation
of tar for road - mending purposes.    The
officers occupy any room which may be available within the farmhouse itself.    The Company Commander has the best bedroom—a
low-roofed, stone-floored apartment, with a
very small window and a very large bed.
The subalterns sleep where they can—usually
in the *grenier*, a loft under the tiles, devoted
to the storage of onions and the drying,
during the winter months, of the family
washing, which is suspended from innumerable strings stretched from wall to wall.

For a Mess, there is usually a spare apartment of some kind.   If not, you put your
pride in your pocket and take your meals at
the kitchen table, at such hours as the family
are not sitting humped round the same with
their hats on, partaking of soup or coffee.
(This appears to be their sole sustenance.)

A farm kitchen in Northern France is a scrupulously clean place—the whole family gets up at half-past four in the morning and sees to the matter—and despite the frugality of her own home *menu*, the *fermière* can produce you a perfect omelette at any hour of the day or night.

This brings us to the kitchen stove, which is a marvel. No massive and extravagant English ranges here! There is only one kind: we call it the Coffin and Flower-pot. The coffin—small, black, and highly polished —projects from the wall about four feet, the further end being supported by what looks like an ornamental black flower-pot standing on a pedestal. The coffin is the oven, and the flower-pot is the stove. Given a handful of small coal or charcoal, Madame appears capable of keeping it at work all day, and of boiling, baking, or roasting you innumerable dishes.

Then there is the family. Who or what they all are, and where they all sleep, is a profound mystery. The family tree is usually headed by a decrepit and ruminant old gentleman in a species of yachting-cap. He sits behind the stove—not exactly with one foot in the grave, but with both knees well up against the coffin—and occasionally offers a mumbled observation of which no one takes the slightest notice. Sometimes, too, there is an old, a very old, lady. Probably she is some one's grandmother, or great-grandmother, but she does not appear to be related to the old gentleman. At least, they never recognise one another's existence in any way.

There are also vague people who possess the power of becoming invisible at will. They fade in and out of the house like wraiths : their one object in life appears to be to efface themselves as much as possible. Madame refers to them as "*refugiés*" : this the sophisticated Mr Cockerell translates, "German spies."

Next in order come one or two farm-hands —usually addressed as "'Nri!" and "'Seph!" They are not as a rule either attractive in appearance or desirable in character. Every man in this country, who *is* a man, is away, as a matter of course, doing a man's only possible duty under the circumstances. This leaves 'Nri and 'Seph, who through physical or mental shortcomings are denied the proud

privilege, and shamble about in the muck and
mud of the farm, leering or grumbling, while
Madame exhorts them to further activity
from the kitchen door. They take their
meals with the family : where they sleep no
one knows. External evidence suggests the
cowhouse.

Then, the family. First, Angèle. She
may be twenty - five, but is more probably
fifteen. She acts as Adjutant to Madame,
and rivals her mother as deliverer of sustained
and rapid recitative. She milks the cows,
feeds the pigs, and dragoons her young
brothers and sisters. But though she works
from morning till night, she has always time
for a smiling salutation to all ranks. She
also speaks English quite creditably—a fact
of which Madame is justly proud. "Collége !"
explains the mother, full of appreciation for
an education which she herself has never
known, and taps her learned daughter affectionately upon the head.

Next in order comes Emile. He must be
about fourteen, but War has forced manhood
on him. All day long he is at work, bullying
very large horses, digging, hoeing, even
ploughing. He is very much a boy, for all

that. He whistles excruciatingly — usually English music-hall melodies—grins sheepishly at the officers, and is prepared at any moment to abandon the most important tasks in order to watch a man cleaning a rifle or oiling a machine-gun. We seem to have encountered Emile in other countries than this.

After Emile, Gabrielle. Her age is probably seven. If you were to give her a wash and brush-up, dress her in a gauzy frock, and exchange her thick woollen stockings and wooden sabots for silk and dancing slippers, she would make a very smart little fairy. Even in her native state she is a most attractive young person, of an engaging coyness. If you say, "Bonjour, Gabrielle!" she whispers, "B'jour M'sieur le Capitaine"—or, "M'sieur le Caporal"; for she knows all badges of rank—and hangs her head demurely. But presently, if you stand quite still and look the other way, Gabrielle will sidle up to you and squeeze your hand. This is gratifying, but a little subversive of strict discipline if you happen to be inspecting your platoon at the moment.

Gabrielle is a firm favourite with the rank and file. Her particular crony is one Private

Mackay, an amorphous youth with flaming
red hair.   He and Gabrielle engage in lengthy
conversations, which appear to be perfectly
intelligible to both, though Mackay speaks
with the solemn unction of the Aberdonian,
and Gabrielle prattles at express speed in
a *patois* of her own.   Last week some unknown humorist, evidently considering that
Gabrielle was not making sufficient progress
in her knowledge of English, took upon himself to give her a private lesson.   Next
morning Mackay, on sentry duty at the farm
gate, espied his little friend peeping round
a corner.

"Hey, Garibell!" he observed cheerfully.
(No Scottish private ever yet mastered a
French name quite completely.)

Gabrielle, anxious to exhibit her new accomplishment, drew nearer, smiled seraphically,
and replied—

"'Ello, Gingeair!"

Last of the bunch comes Petit Jean, a
chubby and close-cropped youth of about six.
Petit Jean is not his real name, as he himself indignantly explained when so addressed
by Major Wagstaffe.

"Moi, z'ne suis pas Petit Jean; z'suis Maurrrice!"

Major Wagstaffe apologised most humbly, but the name stuck.

Petit Jean is an enthusiast upon matters military. He possesses a little wooden rifle, the gift of a friendly "Écossais," tipped with a flashing bayonet cut from a biscuit-tin; and spends most of his time out upon the road, waiting for some one to salute. At one time he used to stand by the sentry, with an ancient glengarry crammed over his bullet head, and conform meticulously to his comrade's slightest movement. This procedure was soon banned, as being calculated to bring contempt and ridicule upon the King's uniform, and Petit Jean was assigned a beat of his own. Behold him upon sentry-go.

A figure upon horseback swings round the bend in the road.

"Here's an officer, Johnny!" cries a friendly voice from the farm gate.

Petit Jean, as upright as a post, brings his rifle from stand-at-ease to the order, and from the order to the slope, with the epileptic jerkiness of a marionette, and scrutinises the approaching officer for stars and crowns. If he can discern nothing but a star or two, he slaps the small of his butt with ferocious solemnity; but if a crown, or a red hatband, reveals itself, he blows out his small chest to its fullest extent and presents arms. If the salute is acknowledged — as it nearly always is—Petit Jean is crimson with gratification. Once, when a friendly subaltern called his platoon to attention, and gave the order, "Eyes right!" upon passing the motionless little figure at the side of the road, Petit Jean was so uplifted that he committed the military crime of deserting his post while on duty—in order to run home and tell his mother about it.

Last of all we arrive at the keystone of the whole fabric—Madame herself. She is one of the most wonderful women in the world. Consider. Her husband and her eldest son are away—fighting, she knows not where, amid dangers and privations which can only be imagined. During their absence she has to manage a considerable farm, with the help of her children and one or two hired labourers of more than doubtful use or reliability. In

addition to her ordinary duties as a parent
and *fermière*, she finds herself called upon, for
months on end, to maintain her premises as
a combination of barracks and almshouse.
Yet she is seldom cross—except possibly when
the *soldats* steal her apples and pelt the pigs
with the cores—and no accumulations of labour
can sap her energy. She is up by half-past four
every morning; yet she never appears anxious
to go to bed at night. The last sound which
sleepy subalterns hear is Madame's voice, uplifted in steady discourse to the circle round
the stove, sustained by an occasional guttural
chord from 'Nri and 'Seph. She has been
doing this day in, day out, since the combatants settled down to trench warfare.
Every few weeks brings a fresh crop of
tenants, with fresh peculiarities and unknown
proclivities ; and she assimilates them all.

The only approach to a breakdown comes
when, after paying her little bill—you may be
sure that not an omelette nor a broken window
will be missing from the account—and wishing
her " Bonne chance ! " ere you depart, you venture on a reference, in a few awkward, stum-
bling sentences, to the absent husband and son.

Then she weeps copiously, and it seems to do her a world of good.   All hail to you, Madame —the finest exponent, in all this War, of the art of Carrying On! We know now why France is such a great country.

# CHAPTER SIX.

### " YE MERRIE BUZZERS."

PRACTICALLY all the business of an Army in the field is transacted by telephone. If the telephone breaks down, whether by the Act of God or the King's Enemies, that business is at a standstill until the telephone is put right again.

The importance of the disaster varies with the nature of the business. For instance, if the wire leading to the Round Game Department is blown down by a March gale, and your weekly return of Men Recommended for False Teeth is delayed in transit, nobody minds very much—except possibly the Deputy Assistant Director of Auxiliary Dental Appliances. But if you are engaged in battle, and the wires which link up the driving-force in front with the directing-force behind are devastated by a storm of shrapnel, the matter assumes a more—nay, a most—serious aspect. Hence the superlative importance in modern warfare of the Signal Sections of the Royal Engineers tersely described by the rank and file as " The Buzzers," or the " Iddy-Umpties."

During peace-training, the Buzzer on the whole has a very pleasant time of it. Once he has mastered the mysteries of the Sema-phore and Morse codes, the most laborious part of his education is over. Henceforth he spends his days upon some sheltered hillside, in company with one or two congenial spirits, flapping cryptic messages out of a blue-and-white flag at a similar party across the valley.

A year ago, for instance, you might have encountered an old friend, Private M'Micking —one of the original " Buzzers " of "A" Com-pany, and ultimately Battalion Signal Ser-geant — under the lee of a pine-wood near Hindhead, accompanied by Lance - Corporal Greig and Private Wamphray, regarding with languid interest the frenzied efforts of three of their colleagues to convey a message from a sunny hillside three-quarters of a mile away.

" Here a message comin' through, boys,"

announces the Lance-Corporal. "They're in
a sair hurry : I doot the officer will be there.
Jeams, tak' it doon while Sandy reads it."

Mr James M'Micking seats himself upon a
convenient log. In order not to confuse his
faculties by endeavouring to read and write
simultaneously, he turns his back upon the
fluttering flag, and bends low over his field
message-pad. Private Wamphray stands facing him, and solemnly spells out the message
over his head.

"*Tae* G·O·C·—I dinna ken what that means
—R·E·D ; *reid*—A·R·M·Y ; *airmy*—H·A·Z—"

"All richt ; that'll be '*Haslemere*,'" says
Private M'Micking, scribbling down the word.
"Go on, Sandy !"

Private Wamphray, pausing to expectorate,
continues—

"R·E·C·O·N·N·O·I·T·R—Cricky, what a worrd !
Let's hae it repeatit."

Wamphray flaps his flag vigorously—he
knows this particular signal only too well—
and the word comes through again. The
distant signaller, slowing down a little,
continues—

*Reconnoitring patrol reports hostile cavalry
scou—*

"That'll be '*scouts*,'" says the ever-ready M'Micking. "Carry on!"

Wamphray continues obediently—

*Country;* stop; *Have thrown out flank guns;* stop; *Shall I advance or re*—

"—*tire*," gabbles M'Micking, writing it down.

"—*where I am;* stop; *From O.C. Advance Guard;* stop; message ends."

"And aboot time, too!" observes the scribe severely. "Haw, Johnny!"

The Lance-Corporal, who has been indulging in a pleasant reverie upon a bank of bracken, wakes up and reads the proffered message.

"*To G.O.C., Red Army, Hazlemere. Reconnoitring patrol reports hostile cavalry scouts country. Have thrown out flank guns. Shall I advance or retire where I am? From O.C. Advance Guard.*"

"This message doesna sound altogether sense," he observes mildly. "That 'shall' should be 'wull,' onyway. Would it no' be better to get it repeatit? The officer——"

"I've given the 'message-read' signal now," objects the indolent Wamphray.

"How would it be," suggests the Lance-Corporal, whose besetting sin is a *penchant* for emendation, "if we were tae transfair yon stop, and say : *Reconnoitring patrol reports hostile cavalry scouts. Country has thrown out flank guns?*"

"What does that mean ? " inquires M'Micking scornfully.

"I dinna ken ; but these messages about Generals and sic-like bodies——"

At this moment, as ill-luck will have it, the Signal Sergeant appears breasting the hillside. He arrives puffing—he has seen twenty years' service — and scrutinises the message.

"You boys," he says reproachfully, "are an aggravate altogether. Here you are, jumping at your conclusions again ! After all I have been telling you ! See ! That worrd in the address should no' be 'Haslemere' at all. It's just a catch ! It's 'Hazebroucke'—a Gairman city that we'll be capturing this time next year. 'Scouts' is no 'scouts,' but 'scouring' —meaning 'sooping up.' 'Guns' should be 'guarrd,' and 'retire' should be 'remain.' Mind me, now ; next time, you'll be up before the Captain for neglect of duty. Wamphray,

K

give the 'C.I.,' and let's get hame to oor
dinners!"

II.

But "oot here" there is no flag-wagging.
The Buzzer's first proceeding upon entering
the field of active hostilities is to get underground, and stay there.

He is a seasoned vessel, the Buzzer of to-
day, and a person of marked individuality.
He is above all things a man of the world.
Sitting day and night in a dug-out, or a cellar,
with a telephone receiver clamped to his ear,
he sees little; but he hears much, and over-
hears more. He also speaks a language of his
own. His one task in life is to prevent the
letter B from sounding like C, or D, or P, or
T, or V, over the telephone; so he has perverted the English language to his own uses.
He calls B "Beer," and D "Don," and so on.
He salutes the rosy dawn as "Akk Emma,"
and eventide as "Pip Emma." He refers to
the letter S as "Esses," in order to distinguish
it from F. He has no respect for the most
majestic military titles. To him the Deputy

Assistant Director of the Mobile Veterinary Section is merely a lifeless formula, entitled Don Akk Don Emma Vic Esses.

He is also a man of detached mind. The tactical situation does not interest him. His business is to disseminate news, not to write leading articles about it. (*O si sic omnes!*) You may be engaged in a life-and-death struggle for the possession of your own parapet with a Boche bombing party; but this does not render you immune from a pink slip from the Signal Section, asking you to state your reasons in writing for having mislaid fourteen pairs of *boots, gum, thigh*, lately the property of Number Seven Platoon. A famous British soldier tells a story somewhere in his reminiscences of an occasion upon which, in some long-forgotten bush campaign, he had to defend a zareba against a heavy attack. For a time the situation was critical. Help was badly needed, but the telegraph-wire had been cut. Ultimately the attack withered away, and the situation was saved. Almost simultaneously the victorious commander was informed that telegraphic communication with the Base had been restored. A message was already coming through.

"News of reinforcements, I hope!" he remarked to his subordinate.

But his surmise was incorrect. The message said, quite simply :—

*Your monthly return of men wishing to change their religion is twenty - four hours overdue. Please expedite.*

There was a time when one laughed at that anecdote as a playful invention. But we know now that it is true, and we feel a sort of pride in the truly British imperturbability of our official machinery.

Thirdly, the Buzzer is a humorist of the sardonic variety. The constant clash of wits over the wires, and the necessity of framing words quickly, sharpens his faculties and acidulates his tongue. Incidentally he is an awkward person to quarrel with. One black night, Bobby Little, making his second round of the trenches about an hour before "stand-to," felt constrained to send a telephone message to Battalion Headquarters. Taking a good breath—you always do this before entering a trench dug-out—he plunged into the

noisome cavern where his Company Signallers
kept everlasting vigil. The place was in total
darkness, except for the illumination supplied
by a strip of rifle-rag burning in a tin of rifle-
oil. The air, what there was of it, was thick
with large, flat, floating particles of free carbon.
The telephone was buzzing plaintively to itself,
in unsuccessful competition with a well-modu-
lated quartette for four nasal organs, contributed by Bobby's entire signalling staff, who,
locked in the inextricable embrace peculiar to
Thomas Atkins in search of warmth, were
snoring harmoniously upon the earthen floor.

The signaller "on duty"—one M'Gurk—
was extracted from the heap and put under
arrest for sleeping at his post. The enormity
of his crime was heightened by the fact that
two undelivered messages were found upon
his person.

Divers pains and penalties followed. Bobby
supplemented the sentence with a homily upon
the importance of vigilance and despatch.
M'Gurk, deeply aggrieved at forfeiting seven
days' pay, said nothing, but bided his time.
Two nights later the Battalion came out of
trenches for a week's rest, and Bobby, weary

and thankful, retired to bed in his hut at
nine P.M., in comfortable anticipation of a full
night's repose.

His anticipations were doomed to disap-
pointment. He was roused from slumber—
not without difficulty—by Signaller M'Gurk,
who appeared standing by his bedside with a
guttering candle-end in one hand and a pink
despatch - form in the other. The message
said :—

*Prevailing wind for next twenty-four hours
probably S. W., with some rain.*

Mindful of his own recent admonitions,
Bobby thanked M'Gurk politely, and went
to sleep again.

M'Gurk called again at half-past two in
the morning, with another message, which
announced :—

*Baths will be available for your Company
from 2 to 3 p.m. to-morrow.*

Bobby stuffed the missive under his air-
pillow, and rolled over without a word.
M'Gurk withdrew, leaving the door of the
hut open.

His next visit was about four o'clock. This
time the message said :—

*A Zeppelin is reported to have passed over*

*Dunkirk at 5 p.m. yesterday afternoon, proceeding in a northerly direction.*

Bobby informed M'Gurk that he was a fool and a dotard, and cast him forth.

M'Gurk returned at five-thirty, with one more despatch. It said:—

*The expression "Dud" will no longer be employed in official correspondence.*

This time his Company Commander promised him that if he appeared again that night he would be awarded fourteen days' Field Punishment Number One.

The result was that upon sitting down to breakfast at nine next morning, Bobby found upon his plate yet another message—from his Commanding Officer—summoning him to the Orderly-room on urgent matters at eight-thirty.

But Bobby scored the final and winning trick. Sending for M'Gurk and Sergeant M'Micking, he said:—

"This man, Sergeant, appears to be unable to decide when a message is urgent and when it is not. In future, whenever M'Gurk is on night duty, and is in doubt as to whether a message should be delivered at once or put aside till morning, he will come to you and

ask for your guidance in the matter.   Do you
understand?"

"Perfectly, sirr!" replied the Sergeant,
outwardly calm.

"M'Gurk, do *you* understand?"

M'Gurk looked at Bobby, and then round at
Sergeant M'Micking.   He received a glance
which shrivelled his marrow.   The game was
up.   He grinned sheepishly, and answered—

"Yes, sirr!"


### III.

Having briefly set forth the character and
habits of the Buzzer, we will next proceed to
visit the creature in his lair.   This is an easy
feat.   We have only to walk up the communication trench which leads from the reserve line
to the firing line.   Upon either side of the
trench, neatly tacked to the muddy wall by a
device of the hairpin variety, run countless
insulated wires, clad in coats of various colours
and all duly ticketed.   These radiate from
various Headquarters in the rear to numerous
signal stations in the front, and were laid by
the Signallers themselves.   (It is perhaps un-

necessary to mention that that single wire running, in defiance of all regulations, across the top of the trench, which neatly tipped your cap off just now, was laid by those playful humorists, the Royal Artillery.) It follows that if we accompany these wires far enough we shall ultimately find ourselves in a signalling station.

Our only difficulty lies in judicious choice, for the wires soon begin to diverge up numerous byways. Some go to the fire-trench, others to the machine-guns, others again to observation posts — whence a hawk-eyed Forward Observing Officer, peering all day through a chink in a tumble-down chimney or sandbagged loophole, is sometimes enabled to flash back the intelligence that he can discern transport upon such a road in rear of the Boche trenches, and will such a battery kindly attend to the matter at once?

However, chance guides us to the Signal dug-out of "A" Company, where, by the best fortune in the world, Private M'Gurk in person is installed as officiating sprite. Let us render ourselves invisible, sit down beside him, and "tap" his wire.

In the dim and distant days before such

phrases as " Boche," and "T.N.T.," and "munitions," and " economy " were invented ; when
we lived in houses which possessed roofs, and
never dreamed of lying down motionless by
the roadside when we heard a taxi-whistle
blown thrice, in order to escape the notice of
approaching aeroplanes—in short, in the days
immediately preceding the war—some of us
said in our haste that the London Telephone
Service was The Limit.  Since then we have
made the acquaintance of the military field
telephone, and we feel distinctly softened towards the young woman at home who, from
her dug-out in " Gerrard," or " Vic.," or
" Hop.," used to goad us to impotent frenzy.
She was at least terse and decided.  If you
rang her up and asked for a number, she
merely replied—

    (*a*)  " Number engaged."

    (*b*)  " No reply."

    (*c*)  " Out of order,"

—as the case might be, and switched you off.
After that you took a taxi to the place with
which you wished to communicate, and there
was an end of the matter.  Above all, she
never explained, she never wrangled, she
spoke tolerably good English, and there was

only one of her—or at least she was of a uniform type.

Now, if you put your ear to the receiver of a field-telephone, you find yourself, as it were, suddenly thrust into a vast subterranean cavern, filled with the wailings of the lost, the babblings of the feeble-minded, and the profanity of the exasperated. If you ask a high-caste Buzzer—say, an R.E. Signalling Officer—why this should be so, he will look intensely wise and recite some solemn gibberish about earthed wires and induced currents.

The noises are of two kinds, and one supplements the other. The human voice supplies the libretto, while the accompaniment is provided by a syncopated and tympanum-piercing *ping-ping*, suggestive of a giant mosquito singing to its young.

The instrument with which we are contending is capable (in theory) of transmitting a message either telephonically or telegraphically. In practice, this means that the signaller, having wasted ten sulphurous minutes in a useless attempt to convey information through the medium of the human voice, next proceeds, upon the urgent advice of the gentle-

man at the other end, and to the confusion of
all other inhabitants of the cavern, to "buzz"
it, adapting the dots and dashes of the Morse
code to his purpose.

It is believed that the wily Boche, by means
of ingenious and delicate instruments, is able
to "tap" a certain number of our trench telephone messages. If he does, his daily Intelligence Report must contain some surprising
items of information. At the moment when
we attach our invisible apparatus to Mr
M'Gurk's wire, the Divisional Telephone
system appears to be fairly evenly divided
between—

(1) A Regimental Headquarters endeavouring to ring up its Brigade.

(2) A glee-party of Harmonious Blacksmiths, indulging in The Anvil Chorus.

(3) A choleric Adjutant, on the track of a
peccant Company Commander.

(4) Two Company Signallers, engaged in a
friendly chat from different ends of the trench
line.

(5) An Artillery F.O.O., endeavouring to
convey pressing and momentous information
to his Battery, two miles in rear.

(6) The Giant Mosquito aforesaid.

The consolidated result is something like this :—

*Regimental Headquarters (affably).* Hallo, Brigade! Hallo, Brigade! HALLO, BRIGADE!

*The Mosquito.* Ping!

*The Adjutant (from somewhere in the Support Line, fiercely).* Give me B Company!

*The Forward Observing Officer (from his eyrie).* Is that C Battery? There's an enemy working party——

*First Chatty Signaller (from B Company's Station).* Is that yoursel', Jock? How's a' wi' you?

*Second Chatty Signaller (from D Company's Station).* I'm daen fine! How's your——

*Regimental Headquarters.* HALLO, BRIGADE!

*The Adjutant.* Is that B Company?

*A Mysterious and Distant Voice (politely).* No, sir; this is Akk and Esses Aitch.

*The Adjutant (furiously).* Then for the Lord's sake get off the line!

*The Mosquito.* Ping! Ping!

*The Adjutant.* And stop that —— —— —— buzzing!

*The Mosquito.* Ping! Ping! Ping!

*The F.O.O.* Is that C Battery? There's

———

*First Chatty Signaller (peevishly).* What's that you're sayin'?

*The F.O.O. (perseveringly).* Is that C Battery? There's an enemy working party in a coppice at——

*First Chatty Signaller.* This is Beer Company, sir. Weel, Jock, did ye get a quiet nicht?

*Second Chatty Signaller.* Oh, aye. There was a wee——

*The F.O.O.* Is that C Battery? There's

———

*Second Chatty Signaller.* No, sir. This is Don Company. Weel, Jimmy, there was a couple of whish-bangs came intil——

*Regimental Headquarters.* HALLO, BRIGADE!

*A Cheerful Cockney Voice.* Well, my lad, what abaht it?

*Regimental Headquarters (getting to work at once).* Hold the line, Brigade. Message to Staff Captain. "Ref. your S.C. fourr stroke seeven eight six, the worrking parrty in question——"

*The F.O.O. (seeing a gleam of hope).*

Working party? Is that C Battery? I
want to speak to——

The Adjutant. 
Brigade Head-
    quarters.     } Get off the line!
Regimental Head-
    quarters.

*First Chatty Signaller.* Haw, Jock, was
ye hearin' aboot Andra?

*Second Chatty Signaller.* No. Whit was
that?

*First Chatty Signaller.* Weel——

*The F.O.O.* (*doggedly*). Is that C Battery?

*Regimental Headquarters* (*resolutely*). " The
worrking parrty in question was duly detailed
for tae proceed to the rendiss vowse at "——

*The Adjutant.* Is that B Company, curse
you?

*Regimental Headquarters* (*quite impervious
to this sort of thing*). —" the rendiss vowse, at
seeven thirrty akk emma, at point H two B
eight nine, near the cross-roads by the Estamint Repose dee Bicyclistees, for tae "—honk!
horkle! honk!

*Brigade Headquarters* (*compassionately*).
You're makin' a 'orrible mess of this message,
ain't you? Shake your transmitter, do!

*Regimental Headquarters (after dutifully performing this operation).* Honkle, honkle, honk. Yang!

*Brigade Headquarters.* Buzz it, my lad, buzz it!

*Regimental Headquarters (dutifully).* Ping, ping! Ping, ping! Ping, ping, ping! Ping——

*General Chorus.* Stop that ——, ——, ——, —— buzzing!

*First Chatty Signaller.* Weel, Andra says tae the Sergeant-Major of Beer Company, says he——

*The Adjutant.* Is that B Company?

*First Chatty Signaller.* No, sir; this is Beer Company.

*The Adjutant (fortissimo).* I *said* Beer Company!

*First Chatty Signaller.* Oh! I thocht ye meant Don Company, sir.

*The Adjutant.* Why the blazes haven't you answered me sooner?

*First Chatty Signaller (tactfully).* There was other messages comin' through, sir.

*The Adjutant.* Well, get me the Company Commander.

*First Chatty Signaller.* Varra good, sirr.

*A pause. Regimental Headquarters being engaged in laboriously "buzzing" its message through to the Brigade, all other conversation is at a standstill. The Harmonious Blacksmiths seize the opportunity to give a short selection. Presently, as the din dies down—*

*The F.O.O. (faint, yet pursuing).* Is that C Battery?

*A Jovial Voice.* Yes.

*The F.O.O.* What a shock! I thought you were all dead. Is that you, Chumps?

*The Jovial Voice.* It is. What can I do for you this morning?

*The F.O.O.* You can boil your signal sentry's head!

*The Jovial Voice.* What for?

*The F.O.O.* For keeping me waiting.

*The Jovial Voice.* Righto! And the next article?

*The F.O.O.* There's a Boche working party in a coppice two hundred yards west of a point——

*The Mosquito (with renewed vigour).* Ping, ping!

*The F.O.O. (savagely).* Shut up!

*The Jovial Voice.* Working party? I'll settle them. What's the map reference?

L

*The F.O.O.* They are in Square number——

*The Harmonious Blacksmiths* (*suddenly and stunningly*). Whang!

*The F.O.O.* Shut up! They are in Square——

*First Chatty Signaller.* Hallo, Headquarters! Is the Adjutant there? Here's the Captain tae speak with him.

*An Eager Voice.* Is that the Adjutant?

*Regimental Headquarters.*—No, sirr. He's away tae his office. Hold the line while I'll——

*The Eager Voice.* No you don't! Put me straight through to C Battery—quick! Then get off the line, and stay there! (*Much buzzing.*) Is that C Battery?

*The Jovial Voice.* Yes, sir.

*The Eager Voice.* I am O.C. Beer Company. They are shelling my front parapet, at L 8, with pretty heavy stuff. I want retaliation, please.

*The Jovial Voice.* Very good, sir. (*The voice dies away.*)

*A Sound over our Heads* (*thirty seconds later*). Whish! Whish! Whish!

*Second Chatty Signaller.* Did ye hear that, Jimmy?

*First Chatty Signaller (with relish).* Mphm!
That'll sorrt them !

*The F.O.O.* Is that C Battery?

*The Jovial Voice.* Yes. What luck, old
son?

*The F.O.O.* You have obtained two direct
hits on the Boche parapet. Will you have a
cocoanut or a ci——

*The Jovial Voice.* A little less lip, my lad !
Now tell me all about your industrious friends
in the coppice, and we will see what we can
do for *them !*

And so on. *A propos* of Adjutants and
Company Commanders, Private Wamphray,
whose acquaintance we made a few pages
back, was ultimately relieved of his position
as a Company Signaller, and returned ignomini-
ously to duty, for tactless if justifiable inter-
position in one of these very dialogues.

It was a dark and cheerless night in mid-
winter. Ominous noises in front of the Boche
wire had raised apprehensive surmises in the
breast of Brigade Headquarters. A forward
sap was suspected in the region opposite the
sector of trenches held by "A" Company.
The trenches at this point were barely forty

yards apart, and there was a very real danger
that Brother Boche might creep under his
own wire, and possibly under ours too, and
come tumbling over our parapet.  To Bobby
Little came instructions to send a specially
selected patrol out to investigate the matter.
Three months ago he would have led the
expedition himself.   Now, as a full-blown
Company Commander, he was officially pre-
cluded from exposing his own most responsible person to gratuitous risks.  So he chose
out that recently-joined enthusiast, Angus
M'Lachlan, and put him over the parapet
on the dark night in question, accompanied
by Corporal M'Snape and two scouts, with
orders to probe the mystery to its depth and
bring back a full report.

It was a ticklish enterprise.  As is frequently the case upon these occasions,
nervous tension manifested itself much more
seriously at Headquarters than in the front-
line trenches.  The man on the spot is, as a
rule, much too busy with the actual execution
of the enterprise in hand to distress himself by speculation upon its outcome.   It
may as well be stated at once that Angus
duly returned from his quest, with an admir-

able and reassuring report. But he was a long time absent. Hence this anecdote.

Bobby had strict orders to report all "developments," as they occurred, to Headquarters by telephone. At half-past eleven that night, as Angus M'Lachlan's colossal form disappeared, crawling, into the blackness of night, his superior officer dutifully rang up Battalion Headquarters, and announced that the venture was launched. It is possible that the Powers Behind were in possession of information as to the enemy's intentions unrevealed to Bobby; for as soon as his opening announcement was received, he was switched right through to a very august Headquarters indeed, and commanded to report direct.

Long-distance telephony in the field involves a considerable amount of "linking-up." Among other slaves of the buzzer who assisted in establishing the necessary communications upon this occasion was Private Wamphray. For the next hour and a half it was his privilege in his subterranean exchange, to sit, with his receiver clamped to his ear, an unappreciative auditor of dialogues like the following :—

" Is that ' A ' Company ? "

" Yes, sir."

" Any news of your patrol ? "

" No, sir."

Again, five minutes later :—

" Is that ' A ' Company ? "

" Yes, sir."

" Has your officer returned yet ? "

" No, sir.  I will notify you when he does."

This sort of thing went on until nearly one o'clock in the morning.  Towards that hour, Bobby, who was growing really concerned over Angus's prolonged absence, cut short his august interlocutor's fifteenth inquiry and joined his sergeant-major on the firing-step. The two had hardly exchanged a few low-pitched sentences when Bobby was summoned back to the telephone.

" Is that Captain Little ? "

" Yes, sir."

" Has your patrol come in ? "

" No, sir."

Captain Little's last answer was delivered in a distinctly insubordinate manner.  Feeling slightly relieved, he returned to the firing - step.  Two minutes later Angus M'Lachlan and his posse rolled over the parapet, safe and sound, and Bobby was able, to his own great content and that of the weary operators along the line, to announce—

"The patrol has returned, sir, and reports everything quite satisfactory. I am forwarding a detailed statement."

Then he laid down the receiver with a happy sigh, and crawled out of the dug-out on to the duck-board.

"Now we'll have a look round the sentries, Sergeant-Major," he said.

But the pair had hardly rounded three traverses when Bobby was haled back to the Signal Station.

"Why did you leave the telephone just now?" inquired a cold voice.

"I was going to visit my sentries, sir."

"But *I* was speaking to you."

"I thought you had finished, sir."

"I had *not* finished. If I had finished, I should have informed you of the fact, and would have said 'Good night!'"

"How *does* one choke off a tripe-merchant of this type?" wondered the exhausted officer.

From the bowels of the earth came the answer to his unspoken question—delivered in a strong Paisley accent—

"For Goad's sake, kiss him, and *say* 'Good Nicht,' and hae done with it!"

As already stated, Private Wamphray was returned to his platoon next morning.

## IV.

But to regard the Buzzer simply and solely as a troglodyte, of sedentary habits and caustic temperament, is not merely hopelessly wrong; it is grossly unjust. Sometimes he goes for a walk—under some such circumstances as the following.

The night is as black as Tartarus, and it is raining heavily. Brother Boche, a prey to nervous qualms, is keeping his courage up by distributing shrapnel along our communication trenches. Signal-wires are peculiarly vulnerable to shrapnel. Consequently no one in the Battalion Signal Station is particularly surprised when the line to "Akk" Company suddenly ceases to perform its functions.

Signal-Sergeant M'Micking tests the instrument, glances over his shoulder, and observes—

"Line BX is gone, some place or other. Away you, Duncan, and sorrt it!"

Mr Duncan, who has been sitting hunched over a telephone, temporarily quiescent, smoking a woodbine, heaves a resigned sigh, extinguishes the woodbine and places it behind his ear; hitches his repairing - wallet nonchalantly over his shoulder, and departs into the night — there to grope in several inches of mud for the two broken ends of the wire, which may be lying fifty yards apart. Having found them, he proceeds to effect a junction, his progress being impeded from time to time by further bursts of shrapnel. This done, he tests the new connection, relights his woodbine, and splashes his way back to Headquarters. That is a Buzzer's normal method of obtaining fresh air and exercise.

More than that. He is the one man in the Army who can fairly describe himself as an indispensable.

In these days, when whole nations are deployed against one another, no commander, however eminent, can ride the whirlwind single-handed. There are limits to individual capacity. There are limits to direct control.

There are limits to personal magnetism. We fight upon a collective plan nowadays. If we propose to engage in battle, we begin by welding a hundred thousand men into one composite giant. We weld a hundred thousand rifles, a million bombs, a thousand machine-guns, and as many pieces of artillery, into one huge weapon of offence, with which we arm our giant. Having done this, we provide him with a brain — a blend of all the experience and wisdom and military genius at our disposal. But still there is one thing lacking—a nervous system. Unless our giant have that,—unless his brain is able to transmit its desires to his mighty limbs,— he has nothing. He is of no account; the enemy can make butcher's-meat of him. And that is why I say that the purveyor of this nervous system—our friend the Buzzer—is indispensable. You can always create a body of sorts and a brain of sorts. But unless you can link the two up, you are foredoomed to failure.

Take a small instance. Supposing a battalion advances to the attack, and storms an isolated, exposed position. Can they hold on, or can they not? That question can only be answered by the Artillery behind them. If the curtain of shell fire which has preceded the advancing battalion to its objective can be "lifted" at the right moment and put down again, with precision, upon a certain vital zone beyond the captured line, counter-attacks can be broken up and the line held. But the Artillery lives a long way—sometimes miles—in rear. Without continuous and accurate information it will be more than useless; it will be dangerous. (A successful attacking party has been shelled out of its hardly won position by its own artillery before now—on both sides!) Sometimes a little visual signalling is possible: sometimes a despatch-runner may get back through the enemy's curtain of fire; but in the main your one hope of salvation hangs upon a slender thread of insulated wire. And round that wire are strung some of the purest gems of heroism that the War has produced.

At the battle of Loos, half a battalion of K (1) pushed forward into a very advanced hostile position. There they hung, by their teeth. Their achievement was great; but unless Headquarters could be informed of their exact position and needs, they were all dead men. So Corporal Greig set out to find them, unreeling wire as he went. He was blown to pieces by an eight-inch shell, but another signaller was never lacking to take his place. They pressed forward, these lackadaisical non-combatants, until the position was reached and communication established. Again and again the wire was cut by shrapnel, and again and again a Buzzer crawled out to find the broken ends and piece them together. And ultimately, the tiny exposed limb in front having been enabled to explain its exact requirements to the brain behind, the necessary help was forthcoming and the Fort was held.

Next time you pass a Signaller's dug-out, peep inside. You will find it occupied by a coke brazier, emitting large quantities of carbon monoxide, and an untidy gentleman in khaki, with a blue-and-white device upon his shoulder-straps, brooding over a small black instrument, and luxuriating in a "frowst" most indescribable. He is reading a back number of a rural Scottish newspaper which you never heard of. Occasionally, in response to a faint buzz, he takes up his transmitter and indulges in an unintelligible altercation with a person unseen. You need feel no surprise if he is wearing the ribbon of the Distinguished Conduct Medal.

# CHAPTER SEVEN.

## PASTURES NEW.

THE outstanding feature of to-day's intelligence is that spring is coming—has come, in fact.

It arrived with a bump. March entered upon its second week with seven degrees of frost and four inches of snow. We said what was natural and inevitable to the occasion ; wrapped our coats of skins more firmly round us ; and made a point of attending punctually when the rum ration was issued.

Forty - eight hours later winter had disappeared. The sun was blazing in a cloudless sky. Aeroplanes were battling for photographic rights overhead ; the brown earth beneath our feet was putting forth its first blades of tender green. The muck - heap

outside our rest-billet displayed unmistakable
signs of upheaval from its winter sleep.
Primroses appeared in Bunghole Wood;
larks soared up into the sky above No Man's
Land, making music for the just and the
unjust. Snipers, smiling cheerfully over the
improved atmospheric conditions, polished up
their telescopic sights. The artillery on each
side hailed the birth of yet another season of
fruitfulness and natural increase with some
more than usually enthusiastic essays in
mutual extermination. Half the Mess caught
colds in their heads.

Frankly, we are not sorry to see the end of
winter. Cæsar, when he had concluded his
summer campaign, went into winter quarters.
Cæsar, as Colonel Kemp once huskily remarked, knew something!

Still, each man to his taste. Corporal
Mucklewame, for one, greatly prefers winter
to summer.

" In the winter," he points out to Sergeant
M'Snape, " a body can breathe withoot
swallowing a wheen bluebottles and bum-bees.
A body can aye streitch himself doon under a
tree for a bit sleep withoot getting wasps and
wee beasties crawling up inside his kilt, and

puddocks craw-crawing in his ear! A body
can keep himself frae sweitin'——"

"He can that!" assents M'Snape, whose
spare frame is more vulnerable to the icy
breeze than that of the stout corporal.

However, the balance of public opinion is
against Mucklewame. Most of us are un-
feignedly glad to feel the warmth of the sun
again. That working party, filling sandbags
just behind the machine-gun emplacement, are
actually singing. Spring gets into the blood,
even in this stricken land. The Boche over
the way resents our efforts at harmony.

> *Sing us a song, a song of Bonnie Scotland!*
> *Any old song will do.*
> *By the old camp-fire, the rough-and-ready choir*
> *Join in the chorus too.*
> *"You'll tak' the high road and I'll tak' the low road"—*
> *'Tis a song that we all know,*
> *To bring back the days in Bonnie Scotland,*
> *Where the heather and the bluebells——*

Whang!

The Boche, a Wagnerian by birth and up-
bringing, cannot stand any more of this, so he
has fired a rifle-grenade at the glee party—on
the whole a much more honest and direct

method of condemnation than that practised
by musical critics in time of peace. But he
only elicits an encore. Private Nigg perches
a steel helmet on the point of a bayonet, and
patronisingly bobs the same up and down
above the parapet.

These steel helmets have not previously
been introduced to the reader's notice. They
are modelled upon those worn in the French
Army—and bear about as much resemblance
to the original pattern as a Thames barge to
a racing yacht. When first issued, they were
greeted with profound suspicion. Though
undoubtedly serviceable—they saved many a
crown from cracking round The Bluff the
other day—they were undeniably heavy, and
they were certainly not becoming to the peculiar type of beauty rampant in K(1). On
issue, then, their recipients elected to regard
the wearing of them as a peculiarly noxious
form of "fatigue." Private M'A. deposited
his upon the parapet, like a foundling on a
doorstep, and departed stealthily round the
nearest traverse, to report his new headpiece
"lost through the exigencies of military
service." Private M'B. wore his insecurely
perched upon the top of his Tam-o'-shanter

M

bonnet, where it looked like a very large ostrich egg in a very small khaki nest. Private M'C. set his up on a convenient post, and opened rapid fire upon it at a range of six yards, surveying the resulting holes with the gloomy satisfaction of the vindicated pessimist. Private M'D. removed the lining from his, and performed his ablutions in the inverted crown.

"This," said Colonel Kemp, "will never do. We must start wearing the dashed things ourselves."

And it was so. Next day, to the joy of the Battalion, their officers appeared in the trenches self-consciously wearing what looked like small sky-blue wash-hand basins balanced upon their heads. But discipline was excellent. No one even smiled. In fact, there was a slight reaction in favour of the helmets. Conversations like the following were overheard :—

"I'm tellin' you, Jimmy, the C.O. is no the man for tae mak' a show of himself like that for naething. These tin bunnets must be some use. Wull we pit oors on ?"

"Awa' hame and bile your heid!" replied the unresponsive James.

"They'll no stop a whish-bang," conceded the apostle of progress, "but they would keep off splunters, and a wheen bullets, and—and——"

"And the rain!" supplied Jimmy sarcastically.

This jibe suddenly roused the temper of the other participant in the debate.

"I tell you," he exclaimed, in a voice shrill with indignation, "that these —— helmets are some —— use!"

"And I tell *you*," retorted James earnestly, "that these —— helmets are no —— —— use!"

When two reasonable persons arrive at a controversial *impasse*, they usually agree to differ and go their several ways. But in K (1) we prefer practical solutions. The upholder of helmets hastily thrust his upon his head.

"I'll show you, Jimmy!" he announced, and clambered upon the firing-step.

"And I'll —— well show *you*, Wullie!" screamed James, doing likewise.

Simultaneously the two zealots thrust their heads over the parapet, and awaited results. These came. The rifles of two Boche snipers rang out, and both demonstrators fell heavily backwards into the arms of their supporters.

By all rights they ought to have been killed. But they were both very much alive. Each turned to the other triumphantly, and exclaimed—

"I tellt ye so!"

There was a hole right through the helmet of Jimmy, the unbeliever. The fact that there was not also a hole through his head was due to his forethought in having put on a Tam-o'-shanter underneath. The net result was a truncated "toorie." Wullie's bullet had struck his helmet at a more obtuse angle, and had glanced off, as the designer of the smooth exterior had intended it to do.

At first glance, the contest was a draw. But subsequent investigation elicited the fact that Jimmy in his backward fall had bitten his tongue to the effusion of blood. The verdict was therefore awarded, on points, to Wullie, and the spectators dispersed in an orderly manner just as the platoon sergeant came round the traverse to change the sentry.

## II.

We have occupied our own present trenches
since January. There was a time when this sector of the line was regarded as a Vale of Rest.
Bishops were conducted round with impunity.
Members of Parliament came out for the week-
end, and returned to their constituents with
first-hand information about the horrors of war.
Foreign journalists, and sight-seeing parties
of munition - workers, picnicked in Bunghole
Wood. In the village behind the line, if a
chance shell removed tiles from the roof of a
house, the owner, greatly incensed, mounted a
ladder and put in some fresh ones.

But that is all over now. K(1)—hard-
headed men of business, bountifully endowed
with munitions—have arrived upon the scene,
and the sylvan peace of the surrounding district is gone. Pan has dug himself in.

The trouble began two months ago, when
our Divisional Artillery arrived. Unversed in
local etiquette, they commenced operations by
"sending up"—to employ a vulgar but convenient catch-phrase — a strongly fortified
farmhouse in the enemy's support line. The

Boche, by way of gentle reproof, deposited
four or five small " whizz-bangs " in our front-
line trenches.   The tenants thereof promptly
telephoned to " Mother," and Mother came to
the assistance of her offspring with a salvo of
twelve-inch shells.   After that, Brother Boche,
realising that the golden age was past, sent
north to the Salient for a couple of heavy
batteries, and settled down to shell Bunghole
village to pieces.   Within a week he had
brought down the church tower : within a
fortnight the population had migrated farther
back, leaving behind a few patriots, too deeply
interested in the sale of small beer and picture
post-cards to uproot themselves.   Company
Headquarters in Bunghole Wood ceased to
grow primroses and began to fill sandbags.

A month ago the village was practically
intact.   The face of the church tower was
badly scarred, but the houses were undamaged.
The little shops were open ; children played
in the streets.   Now, if you stand at the
cross-roads where the church rears its roofless
walls, you will understand what the Abomina-
tion of Desolation means.   Occasionally a
body of troops, moving in small detachments
at generous intervals, trudges by, on its way

to or from the trenches. Occasionally a big howitzer shell swings lazily out of the blue and drops with a crash or a dull thud—according to the degree of resistance encountered—among the crumbling cottages. All is solitude.

But stay! Right on the cross-roads, in the centre of the village, just below the fingers of a sign-post which indicates the distance to four French townships, whose names you never heard of until a year ago, and now will never forget, there hangs a large, white, newly painted board, bearing a notice in black letters six inches high. Exactly underneath the board, rubbing their noses appreciatively against the sign-post, stand two mules, attached to a limbered waggon, the property of the A.S.C. Their charioteers are sitting adjacent, in a convenient shell-hole, partaking of luncheon.

"That was a rotten place we 'ad to wait in yesterday, Sammy," observes Number One. "The draught was somethink cruel."

The recumbent Samuel agrees. "This little 'oller is a bit of all right," he remarks. "When you've done strarfin' that bully beef, 'and it over, ole man!"

He leans his head back upon the lip of the shell-hole, and gazes pensively at the notice-board six feet away. It says:—

```
VERY DANGEROUS.
DO NOT
LOITER
HERE.
```

### III.

Here is another cross-roads, a good mile farther forward—and less than a hundred yards behind the fire-trench. It is dawn.

The roads themselves are not so distinct as they were. They are becoming grass-grown: for more than a year—in daylight at least—no human foot has trodden them. The place is like hundreds of others that you may see scattered up and down this countryside—two straight, flat, metalled country roads, running north and south and east and west, crossing one another at a faultless right angle.

Of the four corners thus created, one is—or

was—occupied by an estaminet : you can still see the sign, *Estaminet au Commerce,* over the door. Two others contain cottages—the remains of cottages. At the fourth, facing south and east, stands what is locally known as a "Calvaire,"—a bank of stone, a lofty cross, and a life-size figure of Christ, facing east, towards the German lines.

This spot is shelled every day—has been shelled every day for months. Possibly the enemy suspects a machine-gun or an observation post amid the tumble-down buildings. Hardly one brick remains upon another. And yet—the sorrowful Figure is unbroken. The Body is riddled with bullets —in the glowing dawn you may count not five but fifty wounds—but the Face is untouched. It is the standing miracle of this most materialistic War. Throughout the length of France you will see the same thing.

Agnostics ought to come out here, for a "cure."

## IV.

With spring comes also the thought of the Next Push.

But we do not talk quite so glibly of pushes

as we did. Neither, for that matter, does
Brother Boche. He has just completed six
weeks' pushing at Verdun, and is beginning
to be a little uncertain as to which direction
the pushing is coming from.

No ; once more the military text-books are
being rewritten. We started this War under
one or two rather fallacious premises. One
was that Artillery was more noisy than
dangerous. When Antwerp fell, we rescinded
that theory. Then the Boche set out to
demonstrate that an Attack, provided your
Artillery preparation is sufficiently thorough,
and you are prepared to set no limit to your
expenditure of Infantry, must ultimately
succeed. To do him justice, the Boche supported his assertions very plausibly. His
phalanx bundled the Russians all the way
from Tannenburg to Riga. The Austrians
adopted similar tactics, with similar results.

We were duly impressed. The world last
summer did not quite realise how far the
results of the campaign were due to German
efficiency and how far to Russian unprepared-
ness. (Russia, we realise now, found herself
in the position of the historic Mrs Partington,
who endeavoured to repel the Atlantic with

a mop. This year, we understand, she is in a position to discard the mop in favour of something far, far better.)

Then came — Verdun. Military science turned over yet another page, and noted that against consummate generalship, unlimited munitions, and selfless devotion on the part of the defence, the most spectacular and highly-doped phalanx can spend itself in vain. Military science also noted that, under modern conditions, the capture of this position or that signifies nothing : the only method of computing victory is to count the dead on either side. On that reckoning, the French at Verdun have already gained one of the great victories of all time.

" In fact," said Colonel Kemp, " this war will end when the Boche has lost so many men as to be unable to man his present trench line, and not before."

" You don't think, sir, that we shall make another Push ? " suggested Angus M'Lachlan eagerly. The others were silent : they had experienced a Push already.

" Not so long as the Boche continues to play our game for us, by attacking. If he tumbles to the error he is making, and digs himself in again—well, it may become necessary to draw him. In that case, M'Lachlan, you shall have first chop at the Victoria Crosses. Afraid I can't recommend you for your last exploit, though I admit it must have required some nerve!"

There was unseemly laughter at this allusion. Four nights previously Angus had been sent out in charge of a wiring party. He had duly crawled forth with his satellites, under cover of darkness, on to No Man's Land; and, there selecting a row of "knife-rests" which struck him as being badly in need of repair, had well and truly reinforced the same with many strands of the most barbarous brand of barbed wire. This, despite more than usually fractious behaviour upon the part of the Boche.

Next morning, through a sniper's loophole, he exhibited the result of his labours to Major Wagstaffe. The Major gazed long and silently upon his subordinate's handiwork. There was no mistaking it. It stood out bright and gleaming in the rays of the rising sun, amid its dingy surroundings of rusty ironmongery. Angus M'Lachlan waited anxiously for a little praise.

"Jolly good piece of work," said Major Wagstaffe at last. "But tell me, why have you repaired the Boche wire instead of your own?"

"The only enemy we have to fear," continued Colonel Kemp, rubbing his spectacles savagely, "is the free and independent British voter—I mean, the variety of the species that we have left at home. Like the gentleman in Jack Point's song, 'he likes to get value for money'; and he is quite capable of asking us, about June or July, 'if we know that we are paid to be funny?'—before we are ready. What's your view of the situation at home, Wagstaffe? You're the last off leave."

Wagstaffe shook his head.

"The British Nation," he said, "is quite mad. That fact, of course, has been common property on the Continent of Europe ever since Cook's Tours were invented. But what irritates the orderly Boche is that there is no method in its madness. Nothing you can go upon, or take hold of, or wring any advantage from."

"As how?"

"Well, take compulsory service. For genera-

tions the electorate of our country has been
trained by a certain breed of politician—the
*bandar log* of the British Constitution—to
howl down such a low and degrading business
as National Defence. A nasty Continental
custom, they called it. Then came the War,
and the glorious Voluntary System got to
work."

"Aided," the Colonel interpolated, "by a
campaign of mural advertisement which a
cinema star's press agent would have boggled
at !"

"Quite so," agreed Wagstaffe. "Next,
when the Voluntary System had done its
damnedest—in other words, when the willing
horse had been worked to his last ounce—we
tried the Derby Scheme. The manhood of the
nation was divided into groups, and a fresh
method of touting for troops was adopted.
Married shysters, knowing that at least
twenty groups stood between them and a
job of work, attested in comparatively large
numbers. The single shysters were less reckless—so much less reckless, in fact, that com-
pulsion began to materialise at last."

"But only for single shysters," said Bobbie
Little regretfully.

"Yes; and the married shyster rejoiced accordingly. But the single shyster is a most subtle reptile. On examination, it was found that the single members of this noble army of martyrs were all 'starred,' or 're-served,' or 'ear-marked'—or whatever it is that they do to these careful fellows. So the poor old married shyster who had only attested to show his blooming patriotism and encourage the others, suddenly found himself confronted with the awful prospect of having to defend his country personally, instead of by letter to the halfpenny press. Then the fat was fairly in the fire! The married martyr——"

"Come, come, old man! Not all of them!" said Colonel Kemp. "I have a married brother of my own, a solicitor of thirty-eight, who is simply clamouring for active service!"

"I know that, sir," admitted Wagstaffe quickly. "Thank God, these fellows are only a minority, and a freak minority at that; but freak minorities seem to get the monopoly of the limelight in our unhappy country."

"The whole affair," mused the Colonel, "can hardly be described as a frenzied rally

round the Old Flag. By God," he broke out
suddenly, "it fairly makes one's blood boil!
When I think of the countless good fellows,
married and single, but mainly married, who
left *all* and followed the call of common
decency and duty the moment the War broke
out—most of them now dead or crippled; and
when I see this miserable handful of shirkers,
holding up vital public business while the
pros and cons of their wretched claims to
exemption are considered—well, I almost wish
I had been born a Boche!"

"I don't think you need apply for natural-
isation papers yet, Colonel," said Wagstaffe.
"The country is perfectly sound at heart over
this question, and always was. The present
agitation, as I say, is being engineered by the
more verminous section of our incomparable
daily Press, for its own ends. It makes our
Allies lift their eyebrows a bit; but they are
sensible people, and they realise that although
we are a nation of lunatics, we usually deliver
the goods in the end. As for the Boche, poor
fellow, the whole business makes him perfectly rabid. Here he is, with all his splendid
organisation and brutal efficiency, and he
can't even knock a dent into our undisci-

plined, back-chatting, fool-ridden, self-depre-
ciating old country! I, for one, sympathise
with the Boche profoundly. On paper, we
don't *deserve* to win!"

"But we shall!" remarked that single-
minded paladin, Bobby Little.

"Of course we shall! And what's more,
we are going to derive a national benefit out
of this War which will in itself be worth the
price of admission!"

"How?" asked several voices.

Wagstaffe looked round the table. The
Battalion were for the moment in Divisional
Reserve, and consequently out of the trenches.
Some one had received a box of Coronas from
home, and the mess president had achieved
a bottle of port. Hence the present symposium at Headquarters Mess. Wagstaffe's
eyes twinkled.

"Will each officer present," he said,
"kindly name his pet aversion among his
fellow-creatures?"

"A person or a type?" asked Mr Waddell
cautiously.

"A type!"

Colonel Kemp led off.

"Male ballet-dancers," he said.

N

"Fat, shiny men," said Bobby Little, "with walrus moustaches!"

"All conscientious objectors, passive resisters, and other cranks!" continued the orthodox Waddell.

"All people who go on strike during wartime," said the Adjutant. There was an approving murmur—then silence.

"Your contribution, M'Lachlan?" said Wagstaffe.

Angus, who had kept silence from shyness, suddenly blazed out—

"I think," he said, "that the most contemptible people in the world to-day are those politicians and others who, in years gone by, systematically cried down anything in the shape of national defence or national inclination to personal service, because they saw there were no *votes* in such a programme; and who *now*"—Angus's passion rose to fever-heat—"stand up and endeavour to cultivate popular favour by reviling the Ministry and the Army for want of preparedness and initiative. Such men do not deserve to live! Oh, sirs——"

But Angus's peroration was lost in a storm of applause.

"You are adjudged to have hit the bull's-eye, M'Lachlan," said Colonel Kemp. "But tell us, Wagstaffe, your exact object in compiling this horrible catalogue."

"Certainly. It is this. Universal Service is a *fait accompli* at last, or is shortly going to be—and without anything very much in the way of exemption either. When it comes, just think of it! All these delightful people whom we have been enumerating will have to toe the line at last. For the first time in their little lives they will learn the meaning of discipline, and fresh air, and *esprit de corps*. Isn't that worth a War? If the present scrap can only be prolonged for another year, our country will receive a tonic which will carry it on for another century. Think of it! Great Britain, populated by men who have actually been outside their own parish; men who know that the whole is greater than the part; men who are too wide awake to go on doing just what the *bandar log* tell them, and allow themselves to be used as stalking-horses for low-down political ramps! When *we*, going round in bath - chairs and on crutches, see that sight —well, I don't think we shall regret our

missing arms and legs quite so much, Colonel.
War is Hell, and all that; but there is one
worse thing than a long war, and that is a
long peace!"

"I wonder!" said Colonel Kemp reflectively. He was thinking of his wife and
four children in distant Argyllshire.

But the rapt attitude and quickened breath
of Temporary Captain Bobby Little endorsed
every word that Major Wagstaffe had spoken.
As he rolled into his "flea-bag" that night,
Bobby re-quoted to himself, for the hundredth
time, a passage from Shakespeare which had
recently come to his notice. He was not a
Shakesperian scholar, nor indeed a student
of literature at all; but these lines had
been sent to him, cut out of a daily
almanac, by an equally unlettered and very
adorable confidante at home :—

" And gentlemen in England, now abed,
    Shall think themselves accursed they were not here,
    And hold their manhoods cheap whiles any speaks
    That fought with us upon Saint Crispin's day !"

Bobby was the sort of person who would
thoroughly have enjoyed the Battle of
Agincourt.

# CHAPTER EIGHT.

## "THE NON-COMBATANT."

WE will call the village St Gregoire. That
is not its real name; because the one thing
you must not do in war - time is to call a
thing by its real name. To take a hackneyed
example, you do not call a spade a spade :
you refer to it, officially, as *Shovels, General
Service, One*. This helps to deceive, and
ultimately to surprise, the enemy; and as
we all know by this time, surprise is the
essence of successful warfare. On the same
principle, if your troops are forced back
from their front-line trenches, you call this
"successfully straightening out an awkward
salient."

But this by the way. Let us get back to
St Gregoire. Hither, mud-splashed, ragged,

hollow-cheeked, came our battalion—they call
us the Seventh Hairy Jocks nowadays—after
four months' continuous employment in the
firing line.    Ypres was a household word
to them; Plugstreet was familiar ground;
Givenchy they knew intimately; Loos was
their wash-pot—or rather, a collection of
wash-pots, for in winter all the shell-craters
are full to overflowing.    In addition to
their prolonged and strenuous labours in the
trenches, the Hairy Jocks had taken part
in a Push—a part not altogether unat-
tended with glory, but prolific in casualties.
They had not been "pulled out" to rest
and refit for over six months, for Divisions
on the Western Front were not at that
period too numerous, the voluntary system
being at its last gasp, while the legions of
Lord Derby had not yet crystallised out of
the ocean of public talk which held them in
solution.    So the Seventh Hairy Jocks were
bone-tired.    But they were as hard as a
rigorous winter in the open could make
them, and — they were going back to rest
at last.    Had not their beloved C.O. told
them so?    And he had added, in a voice
not altogether free from emotion, that if

ever men deserved a solid rest and a good time, "you boys do!"

So the Hairy Jocks trudged along the long, straight, nubbly French road, well content, speculating with comfortable pessimism as to the character of the billets in which they would find themselves.

Meanwhile, ten miles ahead, the advance party were going round the town in quest of billets.

Billet-hunting on the Western Front is not quite so desperate an affair as hunting for lodgings at Margate, because in the last extremity you can always compel the inhabitants to take you in—or at least, exert pressure to that end through the *Mairie*. But at the best one's course is strewn with obstacles, and fortunate is the Adjutant who has to his hand a subaltern capable of finding lodgings for a thousand men without making a mess of it.

The billeting officer on this, as on most occasions, was our friend Cockerell—affectionately known to the entire Battalion as "Sparrow"—and his qualifications for the post were derived from three well-marked and invaluable characteristics — namely, an imperious

disposition, a thick skin, and an attractive
*bonhomie* of manner.

Behold him this morning dismounting from
his horse in the *place* of St Gregoire. Around
him are grouped his satellites—the Quartermaster - Sergeant, four Company Sergeants,
some odd orderlies, and a forlorn little man
in a neat drab uniform with light-blue facings
—the regimental interpreter. The party have
descended, with the delicate care of those
who essay to perform acrobatic feats in kilts,
from bicycles — serviceable but appallingly
heavy machines of Government manufacture,
the property of the "Buzzers," but com-
mandeered for the occasion. The Quartermaster Sergeant, who is not accustomed to
strenuous exercise, mops his brow and glances
expectantly round the *place*. His eye comes
gently to rest upon a small but hospitable-
looking *estaminet*.

Lieutenant Cockerell examines his wrist-
watch.

" Half-past ten ! " he announces. " Quartermaster-Sergeant ! "

" Sirr ! " The Quartermaster-Sergeant un-
glues his longing gaze from the *estaminet*
and comes woodenly to attention.

" I am going to see the Town Major about a billeting area. I will meet you and the party here in twenty minutes."

Master Cockerell trots off on his mud-splashed steed, followed by the respectful and appreciative salutes of his followers—appreciative, because a less considerate officer would have taken the whole party direct to the Town Major's office and kept them standing in the street, wasting moments which might have been better employed elsewhere, until it was time to proceed with the morning's work.

" How strong are you ? " inquired the Town Major.

Cockerell told him. The Town Major whistled.

" That all ? Been doing some job of work, haven't you ? "

Cockerell nodded, and the Town Major proceeded to examine a large-scale plan of St Gregoire, divided up into different-coloured plots.

" We are rather full up at present," he said ; " but the Cemetery Area is vacant. The Seventeenth Geordies moved out yesterday.

You can have that." He indicated a tri-
angular section with his pencil.

Master Cockerell gave a little deprecatory
cough.

"We have come here, sir," he intimated
dryly, "for a change of scene."

The stout Town Major—all Town Majors
are stout—chuckled.

"Not bad for a Scot!" he conceded. "But
it's quite a cheery district, really. You won't
have to doss down in the cemetery itself, you
know. These two streets here"—he flicked a
pencil—"will hold practically all your battalion, at its present strength. There's a
capital house in the Rue Jean Jacques Rousseau which will do for Battalion Headquarters.
The corporal over there will give you your
*billets de logement.*"

"Are there any other troops in the area,
sir?" asked Cockerell, who, as already indicated, was no child in these matters.

"There ought not to be, of course. But
you know what the Heavy Gunners and the
A.S.C. are! If you come across any of them,
fire them out. If they wear too many stars
and crowns for you, let me know, and I will
perform the feat myself. You fellows need a

good rest and no worries, I know. Good morning."

At ten minutes to eleven Cockerell found the Quartermaster-Sergeant and party wiping their moustaches and visibly refreshed, at the exact spot where he had left them; and the hunt for billets began.

"A" Company were easily provided for, a derelict tobacco factory being encountered at the head of the first street. Lieutenant Cockerell accordingly detached a sergeant and a corporal from his train, and passed on. The wants of "B" Company were supplied by commandeering a block of four dilapidated houses farther down the street—all in comparatively good repair except the end house, whose roof had been disarranged by a shell during the open fighting in the early days of the war.

This exhausted the possibilities of the first street, and the party debouched into the second, which was long and straggling, and composed entirely of small houses.

"Now for a bit of the retail business!" said Master Cockerell resignedly. "Sergeant M'Nab, what is the strength of "C" Company?"

"One hunner and thairty-fower other ranks,

sirr," announced Sergeant M'Nab, consulting a much-thumbed roll-book.

"We shall have to put them in twos and threes all down the street," said Cockerell. "Come on; the longer we look at it the less we shall like it. Interpreter!"

The forlorn little man, already described, trotted up, and saluted with open hand, French fashion. His name was Baptiste Bombominet ("or words to that effect," as the Adjutant put it), and may have been so inscribed upon the regimental roll; but throughout the rank and file Baptiste was affectionately known by the generic title of "Alphonso." The previous seven years had been spent by him in the congenial and blameless atmosphere of a Ladies' Tailor's in the west end of London, where he enjoyed the status and emoluments of chief cutter. Now, called back to his native land by the voice of patriotic obligation, he found himself selected, by virtue of a residence of seven years in England, to act as official interpreter between a Scottish Regiment which could not speak English, and Flemish peasants who could not speak French. No wonder that his pathetic brown eyes always appeared full of tears. However, he followed Cockerell down the street, and meekly embarked upon a contest with the lady inhabitants thereof, in which he was hopelessly outmatched from the start.

At the first door a dame of massive proportions, but keen business instincts, announced her total inability to accommodate *soldats*, but explained that she would be pleased to entertain *officiers* to any number. This is a common gambit. Twenty British privates in your *grenier*, though extraordinarily well-behaved as a class, make a good deal of noise, buy little, and leave mud everywhere. On the other hand, two or three officers give no trouble, and can be relied upon to consume and pay for unlimited omelettes and bowls of coffee.

That seasoned vessel, Lieutenant Cockerell, turned promptly to the sergeant and corporal of "C" Company.

"Sergeant M'Nab," he said, "you and Corporal Downie will billet here." He introduced hostess and guests by an expressive wave of the hand. But shrewd Madame was not to be bluffed.

"*Pas de sergents, Monsieur le Capitaine!*" she exclaimed. "*Officiers!*"

"*Ils sont officiers—sous-officiers,*" explained Cockerell, rather ingeniously, and moved off down the street.

At the next house the owner—a small, wizened lady of negligible physique but great staying power—entered upon a duet with Alphonso, which soon reduced that very moderate performer to breathlessness. He shrugged his shoulders feebly, and cast an appealing glance towards the Lieutenant.

"What does she say?" inquired Cockerell.

"She say dis 'ouse no good, sair! She ave seven children, and one *malade*—seek."

"Let me see," commanded the practical officer.

He insinuated himself as politely as possible past his reluctant opponent, and walked down the narrow passage into the kitchen. Here he turned, and inquired—

"Er—*où est la pauvre petite chose?*"

Madame promptly opened a door, and displayed a little girl in bed—a very flushed and feverish little girl.

Cockerell grinned sympathetically at the patient, to that young lady's obvious gratification, and turned to the mother.

"*Je suis très—triste,*" he said; "*j'ai grand*

*misericorde. Je ne placerai pas de soldats ici. Bon jour!"*

By this time he was in the street again. He saluted politely and departed, followed by the grateful regards of Madame.

No special difficulties were encountered at the next few houses. The ladies at the house door were all polite; many of them were most friendly; but naturally each was anxious to get as few men and as many officers as possible—except the proprietress of an *estaminet*, who offered to accommodate the entire regiment. However, with a little tact here and a little firmness there, Master Cockerell succeeded in distributing "C" Company among some dozen houses. One old gentleman, with a black alpaca cap and a six days' beard, proprietor of a lofty establishment at the corner of the street, proved not only recalcitrant, but abusive. With him Cockerell dealt promptly.

"*Ça suffit!*" he announced. "*Montrez-moi votre grenier!*"

The old man, grumbling, led the way up numerous rickety staircases to the inevitable loft under the tiles. This proved to be a noble apartment thirty feet long. From wall to wall stretched innumerable strings.

"We can get a whole platoon in here," said
Cockerell contentedly. "Tell him, Alphonso.
These people," he explained to Sergeant
M'Nab, "always dislike giving up their lofts,
because they hang their laundry there in
winter. However, the old boy must lump it.
After all, we are in this country for his health,
not ours; and he gets paid for every man
who sleeps here. That fixes 'C' Company.
Now for 'D'! The other side of the street
this time."

Quarters were found in due course for "D"
Company; after which Cockerell discovered a
vacant building - site which would serve for
transport lines. An empty garage was marked
down for the Quartermaster's ration store, and
the Quartermaster-Sergeant promptly faded
into its recesses with a grateful sigh. An
empty shop in the Rue Jean Jacques Rousseau, conveniently adjacent to Battalion
Headquarters, was appropriated for that gre-
garious band, the regimental signallers and
telephone section; while a suitable home for
the Anarchists, or Bombers, together with
their stock-in-trade, was found in the basement of a remote dwelling on the outskirts of
the area.

After this, Lieutenant Cockerell, left alone with Alphonso and the orderly in charge of his horse, heaved a sigh of exhaustion and transferred his attention from his note-book to his watch.

"That finishes the rank and file," he said. "I breakfasted at four this morning, and the Battalion won't arrive for a couple of hours yet. Alphonso, I am going to have an omelette somewhere. I shall want you in half an hour exactly. Don't go wandering off for the rest of the day, pinching soft billets for yourself and the Sergeant-Major and your other pals, as you usually do!"

Alphonso saluted guiltily — evidently the astute Cockerell had "touched the spot" — and was turning away, when suddenly the billeting officer's eye encountered an illegible scrawl at the very foot of his list.

"Stop a moment, Alphonso! I have forgotten those condemned machine-gunners, as usual. *Strafe* them! Come on! Once more into the breach, Alphonso! There is a little side-alley down here that we have not tried."

The indefatigable Cockerell turned down the *Rue Gambetta*, followed by Alphonso, faint but resigned.

"Here is the very place!" announced
Cockerell almost at once. "This house,
Number Five. We can put the gunners
and their little guns into that stable at the
back, and the officer can have a room in the
house itself. *Sonnez*, for the last time before
lunch!"

The door was opened by a pleasant-faced
young woman of about thirty, who greeted
Cockerell — tartan is always popular with
French ladies — with a beaming smile, but
shook her head regretfully upon seeing the
*billet de logement* in his hand. The inevitable
duet with Alphonso followed. Presently
Alphonso turned to his superior.

"Madame is ver' sorry, sair, but an *officier*
is here already."

"Show me the *officier!*" replied the prosaic
Cockerell.

The duet was resumed.

"Madame say," announced Alphonso presently, "that the *officier* is not here now; but
he will return."

"So will Christmas! Meanwhile I am
going to put an Emma Gee officer in here."

Alphonso's desperate attempt to translate
the foregoing idiom into French was inter-

rupted by Madame's retirement into the house,
whither she beckoned Cockerell to follow her.
In the front room she produced a frayed sheet
of paper, which she proffered with an apolo-
getic smile. The paper said—

*This billet is entirely reserved for the
Supply Officer of this District. It is not to be
occupied by troops passing through the town.
By Order.*

Lieutenant Cockerell whistled softly and
vindictively through his teeth.

" Well," he said, " for consummate and concentrated nerve, give me the underlings of
the A.S.C. ! This pot-bellied blighter not
only butts into an area which doesn't belong
to him, but actually leaves a chit to warn
people off the grass even when he isn't here !
He hasn't signed the document, I observe.
That means that he is a newly-joined subaltern, trying to get mistaken for a Brass
Hat ! I'll fix *him !* "

With great stateliness Lieutenant Cockerell
tore the offending screed into four portions, to
the audible concern of Madame. But the
Lieutenant smiled reassuringly upon her.

"*Je vous donnerai un autre, vous savez,*" he assured her.

He sat down at the table, tore a leaf from his Field Service Pocket Book, and wrote :—

*The Supply Officer of the District is at liberty to occupy this billet only at such times as it is not required by the troops of the Combatant Services.*

*Signed,*   F. J. COCKERELL,

*Lieut. & Asst. Adj.,*
*7th B. & W. Highes.*

"That's a pretty nasty one !" he observed with relish. Then, having pinned the insulting document conspicuously to the mantelpiece, he observed to the mystified lady of the house—

"*Voilà, Madame.   Si l'officier reviendra, je le verrai moi-même, avec grand plaisir.   Bon jour !*"

And with this dark saying Sparrow Cockerell took his departure.

II.

The Battalion, headed by their tatterdemalion pipers, stumped into the town in due

course, and were met on the outskirts by the
billeting party, who led the various companies to their appointed place. After inspecting their new quarters, and announcing
with gloomy satisfaction that they were the
worst, dirtiest, and most uncomfortable yet
encountered, everybody settled down in the
best place he could find, and proceeded to
make himself remarkably snug.

Battalion Headquarters and the officers of
"A" Company were billeted in an imposing
mansion which actually boasted a bathroom.
It is true that there was no water, but this
deficiency was soon made good by a string of
officers' servants bearing buckets. Beginning
with Colonel Kemp, who was preceded by an
orderly bearing a small towel and a large
loofah, each officer performed a ceremonial
ablution; and it was a collection of what
Major Wagstaffe termed "bright and bonny
young faces" which collected round the mess
table at seven o'clock.

It was in every sense a gala meal. Firstly,
it was weeks since any one (except Second
Lieutenant M'Corquodale, newly joined, and
addressed, for painfully obvious reasons, as
"Tich") had found himself at table in an

apartment where it was possible to stand
upright. Secondly, the Mess President had
coaxed glass tumblers out of the ancient *con-
cierge;* and only those who have drunk from
enamelled ironware for weeks on end can appreciate the pure joy of escape from the inde-
terminate metallic flavour which such vessels
impart to all beverages. Thirdly, these same
tumblers were filled to the brim with inferior but exhilarating champagne—purchased,
as they euphemistically put in the Supply
Column, "locally." Lastly, the battalion had
several months of hard fighting behind it,
probably a full month's rest before it, and
the conscience of duty done and recognition
earned floating like a halo above it. For the
moment, memories of Nightmare Wood and
the Kidney Bean Redoubt — more especially
the latter—were effaced. Even the sorrowful
gaps in the ring round the table seemed less
noticeable.

The menu, too, was almost pretentious.
First came the *hors d'œuvres* — a tin of
sardines. This was followed by what the
Mess Corporal described as a savoury omelette,
but which the Second-in-Command condemned
as "a regrettable incident."

"It is false economy," he observed dryly to the Mess President, "to employ Mark One [1] eggs as anything but hand-grenades."

However, the tide of popular favour turned with the haggis, contributed by Lieutenant Angus M'Lachlan, from a parcel from home. Even the fact that the mess-cook, an inexperienced æsthete from Islington, had endeavoured to tone down the naked repulsiveness of the dainty with discreet festoons of tinned macaroni, failed to arouse the resentment of a purely Scottish Mess. The next course— the beef ration, hacked into the inevitable gobbets and thinly disguised by a sprinkling of curry powder—aroused no enthusiasm ; but the unexpected production of a large tin of Devonshire cream, contributed by Captain Bobby Little, relieved the canned peaches of their customary monotony. Last of all came a savoury—usually described as *the* savoury— consisting of a raft of toast per person, each raft carrying an abundant cargo of fried potted meat, and provided with a passenger in the shape of a recumbent sausage.

[1] In the British Army each issue of arms or equipment receives a distinctive "Mark." Mark 1 denotes the earliest issue.

A compound of grounds and dish-water, described by the optimistic Mess Corporal as coffee, next made its appearance, mitigated by a bottle of Cointreau and a box of Panatellas ; and the Mess turned itself to more intellectual refreshment. A heavy and long overdue mail had been found waiting at St Gregoire. Letters had been devoured long ago. Now, each member of the Mess leaned back in his chair, straightened his weary legs under the table, and settled down, cigar in mouth, to the perusal of the *Spectator* or the *Tatler*, according to rank and literary taste.

Colonel Kemp, unfolding a week-old *Times*, looked over his glasses at his torpid disciples.

" Where is young Sandeman ? " he inquired. Young Sandeman was the Adjutant.

" He went out to the Orderly-room, sir, five minutes ago," replied Bobby Little.

" I only want to give him to-morrow's Orders. No doubt he'll be back presently. I may as well mention to you fellows that I propose to allow the men three clear days' rest, except for bathing and reclothing. After that we must do Company Drill, good and hard, so as to polish up the new draft, who are due to-morrow. I am going to start a bombing-school, too: at least seventy-five per cent of the Battalion ought to pass the test before we go back to the line. However, we need not rush things. We should be here in peace for at least a month. We must get up some sports, and I think it would be a sound scheme to have a sing-song one Saturday night. I was just saying, Sandeman"—this to the Adjutant, who re-entered the room at that moment—"that it would be a sound——"

The Adjutant laid a pink field-telegraph slip before his superior.

"This has just come in from Brigade Head-quarters, sir," he said. "I have sent for the Sergeant-Major."

The Colonel adjusted his glasses and read the despatch. A deathly, sickening silence reigned in the room. Then he looked up.

"I am afraid I was a bit previous," he said quietly. "The Royal Stickybacks have lost the Kidney Bean, and we are detailed to go up and retake it. Great compliment to the regiment, but a trifle mistimed! You young fellows had better go to bed. Parade at four A.M. sharp! Good-night! Come along to the Orderly-room, Sandeman."

The door closed, and the Mess, grinding the ends of their cigars into their coffee-cups, heaved themselves resignedly to their aching feet.

"There ain't," quoted Major Wagstaffe, "no word in the blooming language for it!"

### III.

The Kidney Bean Redoubt is the key to a very considerable sector of trenches.

It lies just behind a low ridge. The two horns of the bean are drawn back out of sight of the enemy, but the middle swells forward over the skyline and commands an extensive view of the country beyond. Direct observation of artillery fire is possible: consequently an armoured observation post has been constructed here, from which Gunner officers can direct the fire of their batteries with accuracy and elegance. Lose the Kidney Bean, and the boot is on the other leg. The enemy has the upper ground now : he can bring observed artillery fire to bear upon all our tenderest spots behind the line. He can also enfilade our front-line trenches.

Well, as already stated, the Twenty-second
Royal Stickybacks had lost the Kidney Bean.
They were a battalion of recent formation,
stout-hearted fellows all, but new to the refinements of intensive trench warfare. When
they took over the sector, they proceeded to
leave undone various vital things which the
Hairy Jocks had always made a point of
doing, and to do various unnecessary things
which the Hairy Jocks had never done. The
observant Hun promptly recognised that he
was faced by a fresh batch of opponents, and,
having carefully studied the characteristics of
the new-comers, prescribed and administered
an exemplary dose of frightfulness. He
began by tickling up the Stickybacks with
an unpleasant engine called the *minenwerfer*,
which despatches a large sausage-shaped projectile in a series of ridiculous somersaults,
high over No Man's Land into the enemy's
front-line trench, where it explodes and an-
nihilates everything in that particular bay.
Upon these occasions one's only chance of
salvation is to make a rapid calculation as to
the bay into which the sausage is going to
fall, and then double speedily round a traverse
—or, if possible, two traverses—into another.

It is an exhilarating pastime, but presents complications when played by a large number of persons in a restricted space, especially when the persons aforesaid are not unanimous as to the ultimate landing-place of the projectile.

After a day and a night of these aerial torpedoes the Hun proceeded to an intensive artillery bombardment. He had long coveted the Kidney Bean, and instinct told him that he would never have a better opportunity of capturing it than now. Accordingly, two hours before dawn, the Redoubt was subjected to a sudden, simultaneous, and converging fire from all the German artillery for many miles round, the whole being topped up with a rain of those crowning instruments of demoralisation, gas-shells. At the same time an elaborate curtain of shrapnel and high explosive was let down behind the Redoubt, to serve the double purpose of preventing either the sending up of reinforcements or the temporary withdrawal of the garrison.

At the first streak of dawn the bombardment was switched off, as if by a tap; the curtain fire was redoubled in volume; and a massed attack swept across the disintegrated

wire into the shattered and pulverised
Redoubt. Other attacks were launched on
either flank; but these were obvious blinds,
intended to prevent a too concentrated defence
of the Kidney Bean. The Royal Stickybacks
—what was left of them—put up a tough
fight; but half of them were lying dead or
buried, or both, before the assault was launched,
and the rest were too dazed and stupefied by
noise and chlorine gas to withstand—much
less to repel—the overwhelming phalanx that
was hurled against them. One by one they
went down, until the enemy troops, having
swamped the Redoubt, gathered themselves
up in a fresh wave and surged towards
the reserve-line trenches, four hundred yards
distant. At this point, however, they met
a strong counter-attack, launched from the
Brigade Reserve, and after heavy fighting
were bundled back into the Redoubt itself.
Here the German machine-guns had staked
out a defensive line, and the German retirement came to a standstill.

Meanwhile a German digging party, many
hundred strong, had been working madly in
No Man's Land, striving to link up the newly-
acquired ground with the German lines. By

the afternoon the Kidney Bean was not only
"reversed and consolidated," but was actually
included in the enemy's front trench system.
Altogether a well - planned and admirably-
executed little operation.

Forty-eight hours later the Kidney Bean
Redoubt was recaptured, and remains in
British hands to this day. Many arms of
the Service took honourable part in the
enterprise—heavy guns, field guns, trench-
mortars, machine-guns, Sappers and Pioneers,
Infantry in various capacities. But this
narrative is concerned only with the part
played by the Seventh Hairy Jocks.

"Sorry to pull you back from rest,
Colonel," said the Brigadier, when Colonel
Kemp reported; "but the Divisional General
considers that the only feasible way to
hunt the Boche from the Kidney Bean
is to bomb him out of it. That means
trench-fighting, pure and simple. I have
called you up because you fellows know the
ins and outs of the Kidney Bean as no one
else does. The Brigade who are in the line
just now are quite new to the place. Here
is an aeroplane photograph of the Redoubt,
as at present constituted. Tell off your own

bombing parties; make your own dispositions; send me a copy of your provisional Orders; and I will fit my plan in with yours. The Corps Commander has promised to back you with every gun, trench-mortar, culverin, and arquebus in his possession."

In due course Battalion Orders were issued and approved. They dealt with operations most barbarous amid localities of the most homelike sound. Number Nine Platoon, for instance (Commander, Lt. Cockerell), were to proceed in single file, carrying so many grenades per man, up Charing Cross Road, until stopped by the barrier which the enemy were understood to have erected in Trafalgar Square, where a bombing-post and at least one machine-gun would probably be encountered. At this point they were to wait until Trafalgar Square had been suitably dealt with by trench-mortar. (Here followed a paragraph addressed exclusively to the Trench Mortar Officer.) After this the bombers of Number Three Platoon would bomb their way across the Square and up the Strand. Another party would clear Northumberland Avenue, while a Lewis gun raked Whitehall. And so on. Every detail was thought out, down to the composition of the parties which were to "clean up" afterwards—that is, extract the reluctant Boche from various underground fastnesses well known to the extractors. The whole enterprise was then thoroughly rehearsed in some dummy trenches behind the line, until every one knew his exact part. Such is modern warfare.

Next day the Kidney Bean Redoubt was in British hands again. The Hun—what was left of him after an intensive bombardment of twenty-four hours—had betaken himself back over the ridge, *viâ* the remnants of his two new communication trenches, to his original front line. The two communication trenches themselves were blocked and sandbagged, and were being heavily supervised by a pair of British machine-guns. Fighting in the Redoubt itself had almost ceased, though a humorous sergeant, followed by acolytes bearing bombs, was still "combing out" certain residential districts in the centre of the maze. Ever and anon he would stoop down at the entrance of some deep dug-out, and bawl—

"Ony mair doon there? Come away, Fritz! I'll gie ye five seconds. Yin, Twa, Three——"

Then, with a rush like a bolt of rabbits, two or three close-cropped, grimy Huns would scuttle up from below and project themselves from one of the exits,—to be taken in charge by grinning Caledonians wearing "tin hats" very much awry, and escorted back through the barrage to the "prisoners' base" in rear.

All through the day, amidst unremitting shell fire and local counter-attack, the Hairy Jocks re-consolidated the Kidney Bean; and they were so far successful that when they handed over the work to another battalion at dusk, the parapet was restored, the machine-guns were in position, and a number of "knife-rest" barbed-wire entanglements were lying just behind the trench, ready to be hoisted over the parapet and joined together in a continuous defensive line as soon as the night was sufficiently dark.

One by one the members of Number Nine Platoon squelched—for it had rained hard all day—back to the reserve line. They were utterly exhausted, and still inclined to feel a little aggrieved at having been pulled out from rest; but they were well content. They had done the State some service, and they

P

knew it; and they knew that the higher powers knew it too. There would be some very flattering reading in Divisional Orders in a few days' time.

Meanwhile, their most pressing need was for something to eat. To be sure, every man had gone into action that morning carrying his day's rations. But the British soldier, improvident as the grasshopper, carries his day's rations in one place, and one place only—his stomach. The Hairy Jocks had eaten what they required at their extremely early breakfast : the residue thereof they had abandoned.

About midnight Master Cockerell, in obedience to a most welcome order, led the remnants of his command, faint but triumphant, back from the reserve line to a road junction two miles in rear, known as Dead Dog Corner. Here the Battalion was to *rendezvous*, and march back by easy stages to St Gregoire. Their task was done.

But at the cross-roads Number Nine Platoon found no Battalion : only a solitary subaltern, with his orderly. This young Casabianca informed Cockerell that he, Second Lieutenant Candlish, had been left behind to "bring in stragglers."

"Stragglers?" exclaimed the infuriated Cockerell. "Do we look like stragglers?"

"No," replied the youthful Candlish frankly, "you look more like sweeps. However, you had better push on. The Battalion isn't far ahead. The order is to march straight back to St Gregoire and reoccupy former billets."

"What about rations?"

"Rations? The Quartermaster was waiting here for us when we *rendezvoused*, and every man had a full ration and a tot of rum." (Number Nine Platoon cleared their parched throats expectantly.) "But I fancy he has gone on with the column. However, if you leg it you should catch them up. They can't be more than two miles ahead. So long!"


IV.


But the task was hopeless. Number Nine Platoon had been bombing, hacking, and digging all day. Several of them were slightly wounded—the serious cases had been taken off long ago by the stretcher-bearers—and Cockerell's own head was still dizzy from the fumes of a German gas-shell.

He lined up his disreputable paladins in the darkness, and spoke—

"Sergeant M'Nab, how many men are present?"

"Eighteen, sirr." The platoon had gone into action thirty-four strong.

"How many men are deficient of an emergency ration? I can make a good guess, but you had better find out."

Five minutes later the Sergeant reported. Cockerell's guess was correct. The British private has only one point of view about the portable property of the State. To him, as an individual, the sacred emergency ration is an unnecessary encumbrance, and the carrying thereof a "fatigue." Consequently, when engaged in battle, one of the first (of many) things which he jettisons is this very ration. The Quartermaster-Sergeant writes it off as "lost owing to the exigencies of military service," and indents for another.

Lieutenant Cockerell's haversack contained a packet of meat-lozenges and about half a pound of chocolate. These were presented to the Sergeant.

"Hand these round as far as they will go,

Sergeant," said Cockerell. "They'll make a mouthful a man, anyhow. Tell the platoon to lie down for ten minutes : then we'll push off. It's only fifteen miles. We ought to make it by breakfast-time. . . ."

Slowly, mechanically, all through the winter night the victors hobbled along. Cockerell led the way, carrying the rifle of a man with a wounded arm. Occasionally he checked his bearings with map and electric torch. Sergeant M'Nab, who, under a hirsute and attenuated exterior, concealed a constitution of ferro-concrete and the heart of a lion, brought up the rear, uttering fallacious assurances to the faint-hearted as to the shortness of the distance now to be covered, and carrying two rifles.

The customary halts were observed. At ten minutes to four the men flung themselves down for the third time. They had covered about seven miles, and were still eight or nine from St Gregoire. The everlasting constellation of Verey lights still rose and fell upon the eastern horizon behind them, but the guns were silent.

"There might be a Heavy Battery dug in

somewhere about here," mused Cockerell.  " I
wonder if we could touch them for a few tins
of bully.    Hallo, what's that ? "

A distant rumble came from the north, and
out of the darkness loomed a British motor-
lorry, lurching and swaying along the rough
cobbles of the *pavé*.    Some of Cockerell's men
were lying dead asleep in the middle of the
road, right at the junction.    The lorry was
going twenty miles an hour.

"Get into the side of the road, you men ! "
shouted Cockerell, "or they'll run over you.
You know what these M.T. drivers are ! "

With indignant haste, and at the last possible moment, the kilted figures scattered to
either side of the narrow causeway.    The
usual stereotyped and vitriolic remonstrances
were hurled after the great hooded vehicle as
it lurched past.

And then a most unusual thing happened.
The lorry slowed down, and finally stopped, a
hundred yards away.    An officer descended,
and began to walk back.    Cockerell rose to
his weary feet and walked to meet him.

The officer wore a major's crown upon the
shoulder-straps of his sheepskin-lined " British

Warm," and the badge of the Army Service Corps upon his cap. Cockerell, indignant at the manner in which his platoon had been hustled off the road, saluted stiffly, and muttered : "Good morning, sir !"

"Good morning!" said the Major. He was a stout man of nearly fifty, with twinkling blue eyes and a short - clipped moustache. Cockerell judged him to be one of the few remnants of the original Expeditionary Force.

"I stopped," explained the older man, "to apologise for the scandalous way that fellow drove over you. It was perfectly damnable; but you know what these converted taxi-drivers are! This swine forgot for the moment that he had an officer on board, and hogged it as usual. He goes under arrest as soon as we get back to billets."

"Thank you very much, sir," said Master Cockerell, entirely thawed. "I'm afraid my chaps were lying all over the road; but they are pretty well down and out at present."

"Where have you come from?" inquired the Major, turning a curious eye upon Cockerell's prostrate followers.

Cockerell explained. When he had finished, he added wistfully—

"I suppose you have not got an odd tin or two of bully to give away, sir? My fellows are about——"

For answer, the Major took the Lieutenant by the arm and led him towards the lorry.

"You have come," he announced, "to the very man you want. I am practically Mr Harrod. In fact, I am a Corps Supply Officer. How would a Maconochie apiece suit your boys?"

Cockerell, repressing the ecstatic phrases which crowded to his tongue, replied that that was just what the doctor had ordered.

"Where are you bound for?" continued the Major.

"St Gregoire."

"Of course. You were pulled out from there, weren't you? I am going to St Gregoire myself as soon as I have finished my round. Home to bed, in fact. I haven't had any sleep worth writing home about for four nights. It is no joke tearing about a country full of shell-holes, hunting for people who have shifted their ration-dump seven times in four days. However, I suppose things will settle down again, now that you fellows have fired Brother Boche out of the Kidney Bean. Pretty fine work, too! Tell me, what is your strength, here and now?"

"One officer," said Cockerell soberly, "and eighteen other ranks."

"All that's left of your platoon?"

Cockerell nodded. The stout Major began to beat upon the tailboard of the lorry with his stick.

"Sergeant Smurthwaite!" he shouted.

There came a muffled grunt from the recesses of the lorry. Then a round and ruddy face rose like a harvest moon above the tailboard, and a stertorous voice replied respectfully—

"Sir?"

"Let down this tailboard; load this officer's platoon into the lorry; issue them with a Maconochie and a tot of rum apiece; and don't forget to put Smee under arrest for dangerous driving when we get back to billets."

"Very good, sir."

Ten minutes later the survivors of Number Nine Platoon, soaked to the skin, dazed, slightly incredulous, but at peace with all the world, reclined close-packed upon the floor of the swaying lorry. Each man held an open tin of Mr Maconochie's admirable ration between his knees. Perfect silence reigned : a pleasant aroma of rum mellowed the already vitiated atmosphere.

In front, beside the chastened Mr Smee, sat the Major and Master Cockerell. The latter had just partaken of his share of refreshment, and was now endeavouring, with lifeless fingers, to light a cigarette.

The Major scrutinised his guest intently. Then he stripped off his " British Warm " — incidentally revealing the fact that he wore upon his tunic the ribbons of both South African Medals and the Distinguished Service Order — and threw it round Cockerell's shoulders.

" I'm sorry, boy ! " he said. " I never noticed. You are chilled to the bone. Button this round you."

Cockerell made a feeble protest, but was cut short.

" Nonsense ! There's no sense in taking risks after you've done your job."

Cockerell assented, a little sleepily. His

allowance of rum was bringing its usual vulgar but comforting influence to bear upon an exhausted system.

"I see you have been wounded, sir," he observed, noting with a little surprise two gold stripes upon his host's left sleeve—the sleeve of a "non-combatant."

"Yes," said the Major. "I got the first one at Le Cateau. He was only a little fellow; but the second, which arrived at the Second Show at Ypres, gave me such a stiff leg that I am only an old crock now. I was second-in-command of an Infantry Battalion in those days. In these, I am only a peripatetic Lipton. However, I am lucky to be here at all: I've had twenty-seven years' service. How old are you?"

"Twenty," replied Cockerell. He was too tired to feel as ashamed as he usually did at having to confess to the tenderness of his years.

The Major nodded thoughtfully.

"Yes," he said; "I judged that would be about the figure. My son would have been twenty this month, only—he was at Neuve Chapelle. He was very like you in appearance—very. His mother would have been

interested to meet you. You might as well
take a nap for half an hour. I have two
more calls to make, and we shan't get home
till nearly seven. Lean on me, old man. I'll
see you don't tumble overboard. . . ."

So Lieutenant Cockerell, conqueror of the
Kidney Bean, fell asleep, his head resting,
with scandalous disregard for military etiquette, upon the shoulder of the stout
Major.

v.

An hour or two later, Number Nine Platoon,
distended with concentrated nourishment and
painfully straightening its cramped limbs, de-
canted itself from the lorry into a little *cul-
de - sac* opening off the Rue Jean Jacques
Rousseau in St Gregoire. The name of the
*cul-de-sac* was the Rue Gambetta.

Their commander, awake and greatly refreshed, looked round him and realised, with
a sudden sense of uneasiness, that he was
in familiar surroundings. The lorry had
stopped at the door of Number Five.

"I don't suppose your Battalion will get

back for some time," said the Major. "Tell your Sergeant to put your men into the stable behind this house — there's plenty of straw there—and——"

"Their own billet is just round the corner, sir," replied Cockerell. "They might as well go there, thank you."

"Very good. But come in with me yourself, and doss here for a few hours. You can report to your C.O. later in the day, when he arrives. This is my *pied-à-terre*"— rapping on the door. "You won't find many billets like it. As you see, it stands in this little backwater, and is not included in any of the regular billeting areas of the town. The Town Major has allotted it to me permanently. Pretty decent of him, wasn't it? And Madame Vinot is a dear. Here she is! *Bonjour, Madame Vinot! Avez-vous un feu* — er — *inflammé pour moi dans la chambre?*" Evidently the Major's French was on a par with Cockerell's.

But Madame understood him, bless her!

"*Mais oui, M'sieur le Colonel!*" she exclaimed cheerfully—the rank of Major is not recognised by the French civilian population —and threw open the door of the sitting-room, with a glance of compassion upon the Major's mud-splashed companion, whom she failed to recognise.

A bright fire was burning in the open stove.

Immediately above, pinned to the mantel-piece and fluttering in the draught, hung Cockerell's manifesto upon the subject of non - combatants. He could recognise his own handwriting across the room. The Major saw it too.

"Hallo, what's that hanging up, I wonder?" he exclaimed. "A memorandum for me, I expect : probably from my old friend 'Dados.'[1] Let us get a little more light."

He crossed to the window and drew up the blind. Cockerell moved too. When the Major turned round, his guest was standing by the stove, his face scarlet through its grime.

"I'm awfully sorry, sir," said Cockerell, "but that notice — memorandum — of yours has dropped into the fire."

[1] D.A.D.O.S. Deputy Assistant Director of Ordnance Stores.

"If it came from Dados," replied the Major, "thank you very much!"

"I can't tell you, sir," added Cockerell humbly, "what a fool I feel."

But the apology referred to an entirely different matter.

# CHAPTER NINE.

## TUNING UP.

IT is just one year to-day since we "came oot." A year plays havoc with the "establishment" of a battalion in these days of civilised warfare. Of the original band of stout-hearted but inexperienced Crusaders who crossed the Channel in the van of The First Hundred Thousand, in May 1915—a regiment close on a thousand strong, with twenty-eight officers — barely two hundred remain, and most of these are Headquarters or Transport men. Of officers there are five — Colonel Kemp, Major Wagstaffe, Master Cockerell, Bobby Little, and Mr Waddell, who, by the way, is now Captain Waddell, having succeeded to the command of his old Company.

Of the rest, our old Colonel is in Scotland, essaying ambitious pedestrian and equestrian

feats upon his new leg. Others have been
drafted to the command of newer units, for
every member of "K(1)." is a Nestor now.
Others are home, in various stages of con-
valescence. Others, alas! will never go
home again.

But the gaps have all been filled up, and
once more we are at full strength, comfortably conscious that whereas a year ago we
were fighting to hold a line, and play for
time, and find our feet, while the people at
home behind us were making good, now we
are fighting for one thing and one thing
only; and that is, to administer the knock-
out blow to Brother Boche.

Our last casualty was Ayling, who left
us under somewhat unusual circumstances.

Towards the end of our last occupancy of
trenches the local Olympus decided that
what both sides required, in order to
awaken them from their winter lethargy, or
spring lassitude (or whatever it is that
Olympus considers that we in the firing
line are suffering from for the moment), was
a tonic. Accordingly, orders were issued
for a Flying Matinée, or trench raid. Each
battalion in the Division was to submit a

Q

scheme, and the battalion whose scheme
was adjudged the best was to be accorded
the honour—so said the Practical Joke Department — of carrying out the scheme in
person. To the modified rapture of the
Seventh Hairy Jocks, their plan was awarded
first prize. Headquarters, after a little excusable recrimination on the subject of unnecessary zeal and misguided ambition, set
to work to arrange rehearsels of our highly
unpopular production.

Brother Boche has grown " wise " to Flying
Matinées nowadays, and to score a real success you have to present him with something
comparatively novel and unexpected. However, our scheme had been carefully thought
out ; and, given sufficient preparation and an
adequate cast, there seemed no reason to
doubt that the piece would have a highly
successful run of one night.

At one point in the enemy's trenches
opposite to us his barbed-wire defences had
worn very thin, and steps were taken by
means of systematic machine-gun fire to
prevent him from repairing them. This
spot was selected for the raid. A party of
twenty-five was detailed. It was to be led

by Angus M'Lachlan, and was to slip over
the parapet on a given moonless night, crawl
across No Man's Land to within striking
distance of the German trench, and wait. At
a given moment the signal for attack would
be given, and the wire demolished by a
means which need not be specified here.
Thereupon the raiding party were to dash
forward and—to quote the Sergeant-Major—
"mix themselves up in it."

Two elements are indispensable in a successful trench-raid — surprise and despatch.
That is to say, you must deliver your raid
when and where it is least expected, and
then get home to bed before your victims
have had time to set the machinery of retaliation in motion. Steps were therefore
taken, firstly, to divert the enemy's attention
as far as possible from the true objective of
the raid, by a sudden and furious bombardment of a sector of trenches three hundred
yards away; and secondly, to ensure as far
as possible that the raid, having commenced
at two A.M., should conclude at two twelve,
sharp.

In order to cover the retirement of the
excursionists, Ayling was ordered to arrange

for machine-gun fire, which should sweep the
enemy's parapet for some hundreds of yards
upon either flank, and so encourage the enemy
to keep his head down and mind his own
business.

The raid itself was a brilliant success.
Dug-outs were bombed, emplacements destroyed, and a respectable bag of captives
brought over. But the element of surprise,
upon which so much insistence was laid
above, was visited upon both attackers and
attacked. To the former the contribution
came from that well-meaning but somewhat
addle-pated warrior, Private Nigg, who
formed one of the raiding party.

Nigg's allotted task upon this occasion was
to "comb out" certain German dug-outs.
(It may be mentioned that each man had a
specific duty to perform, and a specific portion
of the trench opposite to perform it in; for
the raid had been rehearsed several times in a
dummy trench behind the lines constructed
exactly to scale from an aeroplane photograph.)
For this purpose he was provided with bombs.
Shortly before two o'clock in the morning the
party, headed by Angus M'Lachlan, crawled
over the parapet during a brief lull in the

activities of the Verey lights, and crept steadily, on hands and knees, across No Man's Land. Fifty yards from the enemy's wire was a collection of shell-holes, relics of a burst of misdirected energy on the part of a six-inch battery. Here the raiders disposed themselves, and waited for the signal.

Now, it is an undoubted fact that, if you curl yourself up, with two or three preliminary twirls, after the fashion of a dog going to bed, in a perfectly circular shell-hole, on a night as dark as the inside of a cow, you are extremely likely to lose your sense of direction. This is what happened to Private Nigg. He and his infernal machines lay uneasily in their appointed shell-hole for some ten minutes, surrounded by Verey lights which shot suddenly into the sky with a disconcerting *plop*, described a graceful parabola, burst into dazzling flame, and fluttered sizzling down. One or two of these fell quite near Nigg's party, and continued to burn upon the ground, but the raiders sank closer into their shell-holes, and no alarm resulted. Once or twice a machine-gun had a scolding fit, and bullets whispered overhead. But, on the whole, the night was quiet.

Then suddenly, with a shattering roar, the feint-artillery bombardment broke forth. Simultaneously word was passed along the raiding line to stand by. Next moment Angus M'Lachlan and his followers rose to their feet in the black darkness, scrambled out of their nests, and dashed forward to the accomplishment of their mission.

When Nigg, who had paused a moment to collect his bombs, sprang out of his shell-hole, not a colleague was in sight. At least, Nigg could see no one. However, want of courage was not one of his failings. He bounded blindly forward by himself.

Try as he would he could not overtake the raiding party. However, this mattered little, for suddenly a parapet loomed before him. In this same parapet, low down, Nigg beheld a black and gaping aperture—plainly a loop-hole of some kind.

Without a moment's hesitation, Nigg hurled a Mills grenade straight through the loophole, and then with one wild screech of "Come away, boys!" took a flying leap over the parapet—and landed in his own trench, in the arms of Corporal Mucklewame.

As already noted, it is difficult, when lying

curled up in a circular shell-hole in the dark,
to maintain a true sense of direction.

So the first-fruits of the raid was Captain
Ayling, of the *Emma Gees*. He had stationed
himself in a concrete emplacement in the front
line, the better to "observe" the fire of his
guns when it should be required. Unfortunately this was the destination selected by the
misguided Nigg for his first (and as it proved,
last) bomb. The raiders came safely back in
due course, but by that time Ayling, liberally
(but by a miracle not dangerously) ballasted
with assorted scrap-iron, was on his way to
the First Aid Post.

## II.

At the present moment we are right back
at rest once more, and are being treated with
a consideration, amounting almost to indul-
gence, which convinces us that we are being
"fattened up"—to employ the gruesome but
expressive phraseology of the moment—for
some particularly strenuous enterprise in the
near future.

Well, we are ready. It is nine months

since Loos, and nearly six since we scraped the nightmare mud of Ypres from our boots, *gum, thigh*, for the last time. Our recent casualties have been light—our only serious effort of late has been the recapture of the Kidney Bean—the new drafts have settled down, and the young officers have been blooded. And above all, victory is in the air. We are going into our next fight with new - born confidence in the powers behind us. Loos was an experimental affair; and though to the humble instruments with which the experiment was made the proceedings were less hilarious than we had anticipated, the results were enormously valuable to a greatly expanded and entirely untried Staff.

"We shall do better this time," said Major Wagstaffe to Bobby Little, as they stood watching the battalion assemble, in workmanlike fashion, for a route-march. "There are just one or two little points which had not occurred to us then. We have grasped them now, I think."

"Such as?"

"Well, you remember we all went into the Loos show without any very lucid idea as to how far we were to go, and where to knock off for the day, so to speak. The result was that the advance of each Division was regulated by the extent to which the German wire in front of it had been cut by our artillery. Ours was well and truly cut, so we penetrated two or three miles. The people on our left never started at all. Lord knows, they tried hard enough. But how could any troops get through thirty feet of uncut wire, enfiladed by machine-guns? The result was that after forty-eight hours' fighting, our whole attacking front, instead of forming a nice straight line, had bagged out into a series of bays and peninsulas."

"Our crowd wasn't even a peninsula," remarked Bobby with feeling. "For an hour or so it was an island!"

I think you will find that in the next show we shall go forward, after intensive bombardment, quite a short distance; then consolidate; then wait till the *whole* line has come up to its appointed objective; then bombard again; then go forward another piece; and so on. That will make it impossible for gaps to be created. It will also give our gunners a chance to cover our advance continuously. You remember at Loos they lost us for hours, and dare not fire for fear of hitting us. In fact, I expect that in battle plans of the future, instead of the artillery trying to conform to the movements of the infantry, matters will be reversed. The guns, after preliminary bombardment, will create a continuous Niagara of exploding shells upon a given line, marked in everybody's map, and timed for an exact period, just beyond the objective; and the infantry will stroll up into position a comfortable distance behind, reading the timetable, and dig themselves in. Then the barrage will lift on to the next line, and we shall toddle forward again. That's the new plan, Bobby! Close artillery co-operation, and a series of limited objectives!"

"It sounds all right," agreed Bobby. "We shall want a good many guns, though, shan't we?"

"We shall. But don't let that worry you. It is simply raining guns at the Base now. In fact, my grandmother in the War Office"— this mythical relative was frequently quoted by Major Wagstaffe, and certainly her information had several times proved surprisingly correct—"tells me that by the beginning of next year we shall have enough guns, of various calibres, to make a continuous line, hub to hub, from one end of our front to the other."

"Golly!" observed Captain Little, with respectful relish.

"That means," continued Wagstaffe, "that we shall be able to blow Brother Boche's immediate place of business to bits, and at the same time take on his artillery with counter-battery work. Our shell-supply is practically unlimited now; so when the next push comes, we foot-sloggers ought to have a more gentlemanly time of it than we had at Loos and Wipers. And I'll tell you another thing, Bobby. We shall have command of the air too."

"That will be a pleasant change," remarked Bobby. "I'm getting tired of putting my fellows under arrest for rushing out of carefully concealed positions in order to gape up at Boche planes going over. Angus M'Lachlan is as bad as any of them. The fellow——"

"But you have not seen many Boche planes lately?"

"No. Certainly not so many."

"And the number will grow beautifully less.

Our little friends in the R.F.C. are getting fairly numerous now, and their machines have been improved out of all knowledge. They are rapidly assuming the position of top dog. Moreover, the average Boche does not take kindly to flying. It is too—too individualistic a job for him. He likes to work in a bunch with other Boches, where he can keep step, and maintain dressing, and mark time, if he gets confused. In the air one cannot mark time, and it worries Fritz to death. I think you will see, in the next unpleasantness, that we shall be able to maintain our aeroplane frontier somewhere over the enemy third line. That means that we shall make our own dispositions with a certain degree of privacy, and the Boche will not. Also, when our big guns get to work, they will not need to fire blindly, as in the days of our youth, but will be directed by one of our R.F.C. lads, humming about in his little bus above the target, perhaps fifteen miles from the gun. Hallo, there go the pipes! Tell your men to fall in."

"The whole business," observed Bobby, as he struggled into his equipment, "sounds so attractive that I am beginning quite to look forward to the next show!"

"Don't forget the Boche machine-guns, my lad," replied Wagstaffe.

"One seldom gets the chance," grumbled Bobby. "Is there no way of knocking them out?"

"Well——" Wagstaffe looked intensely mysterious—"Of course one never knows, but—have you heard any rumours on the subject?"

"I have. About——"

"About the Hush! Hush! Brigade?"

Bobby nodded.

"Yes," he said. "Young Osborne, my best subaltern after Angus, disappeared last month to join it. Tell me, what *is* the——?"

"Hush! Hush!" said Major Wagstaffe. "*Méfiez vous! Taisez vous!* and so on!"

The battalion moved off.

So much for the war-talk of veterans. Now let us listen to the novices.

"Bogle," said Angus M'Lachlan to his henchman, "I think we shall have to lighten this Wolseley valise of mine. With one thing and another it weighs far more than thirty-five pounds."

"That's a fact, sirr," agreed Mr Bogle. "It carries ower mony books in the heid of it."

They shook out the contents of the valise
upon the floor of Angus's bedroom—a loft over
the kitchen in A Company's farm billet—and
proceeded to prune Angus's personal effects.
There were boots, socks, shaving-tackle, maps,
packets of chocolate, and books of every size,
but chiefly of the ever - blessed sevenpenny
type.

"A lot of these things will have to go,
Bogle," said Angus regretfully. "The Colonel
has warned officers about their kits, and it
would never do to have mine turned back
from the waggon at the last minute."

Mr Bogle pricked up his ears.

"The waggon? Are we for off again, sir?"
he inquired.

"Indeed I could not say," replied the
cautious Angus; "but it is well to be ready."

"The boys was saying, sirr," observed Bogle
tentatively, "that there was to be another
grand battle soon."

"It is more than likely," said Angus, with
an air of profound wisdom. "Here we are in
June, and we must take the offensive, sooner
or later, or summer will be over."

"What kind o' a battle will it be this time,
sirr?" inquired Bogle respectfully.

"Oh, our artillery will pound the German trenches for a week or two, and then we shall go over the parapet and drive them back for miles," said Angus simply.

"And what then, sirr?"

"What then? We shall go on pushing them until another Division relieves us."

Bogle nodded comprehendingly. He now had firmly fixed in his mind the essential details of the projected great offensive of 1916. He was not interested to go further in the matter. And it is this very faculty—philosophic trust, coupled with absolute lack of imagination—which makes the British soldier the most invincible person in the world. The Frenchman is inspired to glorious deeds by his great spirit and passionate love of his own sacred soil; the German fights as he thinks, like a machine. But the British Tommy wins through owing to his entire indifference to the pros and cons of the tactical situation. He settles down to war like any other trade, and, as in time of peace, he is chiefly concerned with his holidays and his creature comforts. A battle is a mere incident between one set of billets and another. Consequently he does not allow the grim realities of war to obsess his mind when off duty. One might almost ascribe his success as a soldier to the fact that his domestic instincts are stronger than his military instincts.

Put the average Tommy into a trench under fire : how does he comport himself? Does he begin by striking an attitude and hurling defiance at the foe? No, he begins by inquiring, in no uncertain voice, where his —— dinner is? He then examines his new quarters. Before him stands a parapet, buttressed mayhap with hurdles or balks of timber, the whole being designed to preserve his life from hostile projectiles. How does he treat this bulwark? Unless closely watched, he will begin to chop it up for firewood. His next proceeding is to construct for himself a place of shelter. This sounds a sensible proceeding, but here again it is a case of "safety second." A British Tommy regards himself as completely protected from the assaults of his enemies if he can lay a sheet of corrugated-iron roofing across his bit of trench and sit underneath it. At any rate it keeps the rain off, and that is all that his instincts demand of him. An ounce of comfort is worth a pound of security.

He looks about him. The parapet here requires fresh sandbags; there the trench needs pumping out. Does he fill sandbags, or pump, of his own volition? Not at all. Unless remorselessly supervised, he will devote the rest of the morning to inventing and chalking up a title for his new dug-out— "Jock's Lodge," or "Burns' Cottage," or "Cyclists' Rest"—supplemented by a cautionary notice, such as—*No Admittence. This Means You.* Thereafter, with shells whistling over his head, he will decorate the parapet in his immediate vicinity with picture post-cards and cigarette photographs. Then he leans back with a happy sigh. His work is done. His home from home is furnished. He is now at leisure to think about " they Gairmans" again. That may sound like an exaggeration; but " Comfort First" is the motto of that lovable but impudent grasshopper, Thomas Atkins, all the time.

A sudden and pertinent thought occurred to Mr Bogle, who possessed a Martha-like nature.

" What way, sir, will a body get his dinner, if we are to be fighting for twa-three days on end?"

R

"Every man," replied Angus, will be issued, I expect, with two days' rations. But the Colonel tells me that during hard fighting a man does not feel the desire for food—or sleep either, for that matter. Perhaps, during a lull, it may occur to him that he has not eaten since yesterday, and he may pull out a bit of biscuit or chocolate from his pocket, just to nibble. Or he remembers that he has had no sleep for twenty-four hours—so he just drops down and sleeps for ten minutes while there is time. But generally, matters of ordinary routine drop out of a man's thoughts altogether."

"That's a queer-like thing, a body forgetting his dinner!" murmured Bogle.

"Of course," continued Angus, warming to his theme like his own father in his pulpit, "if Nature is expelled with a pitchfork in this manner for too long, *tamen usque recurret.*"

"Is that a fact," replied Bogle politely. He always adopted the line of least resistance when his master took to audible rumination. "Weel, I'll hae to be steppin', sir. I'll pit these twa blankets oot in the sun, in some place where the dooks frae the pond will no'

get dandering ower them. And if you'll sorrt
your books, I'll hand ower the yins ye dinna
require to the Y.M.C.A. hut ayont the village."

Bogle cherished a profound admiration for
Lieutenant M'Lachlan both as a scholar and a
strategist, and absorbed his deliverances with
a care and attention which enabled him to
misquote the same quite fluently to his own
associates. That very evening he set forth
the coming plan of campaign, as elucidated to
him by his master, to a mixed assemblage at
the *Estaminet Au Clef des Champs*. Some of
the party were duly impressed; but Mr Spike
Johnson, a resident in peaceful times of Strat-
ford-atte-Bow, the recognised humourist of
the Sappers' Field Company attached to the
Brigade, was pleased to be facetious.

"It won't be no good you Jocks goin' over
no parapet to attack no 'Uns," he said, "after
what 'appened last week!"

This dark saying had the effect of rousing
every Scottish soldier in the *estaminet* to a
state of bristling attention.

"And what was it," inquired Private Cosh
with heat, "that happened last week?"

"Why," replied Mr Johnson, who had been
compounding this jest for some days, and now

saw his opportunity to deliver it with effect at short range, " your trenches got raided last Wednesday, when you was in 'em. By the Brandyburgers, I think it was."

The entire symposium stared at the jester with undisguised amazement.

" Our —— trenches," proclaimed Private Tosh with forced calm, "were never raided by no —— Brandyburrgerrs ! Was they, Jimmie ? "

Mr Cosh corroborated, with three adjectives which Mr Tosh had not thought of.

Spike Johnson merely smiled, with the easy assurance of a man who has the ace up his sleeve.

" Oh yes, they was ! " he reiterated.

" They werre *not !* " shouted half a dozen voices.

The next stage of the discussion requires no description. It terminated, at the urgent request of Madame from behind the bar, and with the assistance of the Military Police, in the street outside.

" And now, Spike Johnson," inquired Private Cosh, breathing heavily, but much refreshed, " can you tell me what way Gairmans could get intil the trenches of

a guid Scots regiment withoot bein'
*seen ?*"

"I can," replied Mr Johnson with relish,
"and I will. They got in all right, but
you didn't see them, because they was disguised."

Cosh and Tosh snorted disdainfully, and
Private Nigg, who was present with his friend
Buncle, inquired—

"What way was they disguised?"

Like lightning came the answer—

"*As a joke!* Oh, you Jocks!"

Cosh and Tosh (who had already been
warned by the Police sergeant) merely glared
and gurgled impotently. Private Nigg, who,
as already mentioned, was slightly wanting in
quickness of perception, was led away by the
faithful Buncle to have the outrage explained
to him at leisure. It was Private Bogle who
intervened, and brought the intellectual
Goliath crashing to the ground.

"Man, Johnson," he remarked, and shook
his head mournfully, "youse ought to be
varra careful about sayin' things like that to
the likes of us. 'Deed aye!"

"What for, ole son?" inquired the jester
indulgently.

"Naithing," replied Bogle with artistic reticence.

"Come along—aht with it!" insisted Johnson. "Cough it up, duckie!"

"Man, man," cried Bogle with passionate earnestness, "dinna gang ower far!"

"What the 'ell *for?*" inquired Johnson, impressed despite himself.

"What for?" Bogle's voice dropped to a ghostly whisper. "Has it ever occurred to you, my mannie, what would happen tae the English—if Scotland was tae mak' a separate peace?"

And Mr Bogle retired, not before it was time, within the sheltering portals of the *estaminet,* where not less than seven inarticulate but appreciative fellow - countrymen offered him refreshment.

# CHAPTER TEN.

### FULL CHORUS.

An Observation Post—or O Pip, in the mysterious *patois* of the Buzzers—is not exactly the spot that one would select either for spaciousness or accessibility. It may be situated up a chimney, or up a tree, or down a tunnel bored through a hill. But it certainly enables you to see something of your enemy; and that, in modern warfare, is a very rare and valuable privilege.

Of late the scene-painter's art—technically known as *camouflage*—has raised the concealment of batteries and their observation posts to the realm of the uncanny. According to Major Wagstaffe, you can now disguise anybody as anything. For instance, you can make up a battery of six-inch guns to look like a flock of sheep, and herd them into action browsing. Or you can despatch a scouting party across No Man's Land dressed up as pillar-boxes, so that the deluded Hun, instead of opening fire with a machine-gun, will merely post letters in them—valuable letters, containing military secrets. Lastly, and more important still, you can disguise yourself to look like nothing at all, and in these days of intensified artillery fire it is very seldom that nothing at all is hit.

The particular O Pip with which we are concerned at present, however, is a German post—or was a fortnight ago, before the opening of the battle of the Somme.

For nearly two years the British Armies on the Western Front have been playing for time. They have been sticking their toes in and holding their ground, with numerically inferior forces and inadequate artillery support, against a nation in arms which has set out, with forty years of preparation at its back, to sweep the earth. We have held them, and now *der Tag* has come for us. The deal has passed into our hand at last. A fortnight ago, ready for the first time to undertake the offensive on a grand and pro-longed scale—Loos, last September, was a

mere reconnaissance compared with this—the
new British army went over the parapet
shoulder to shoulder with the most heroic
Army in the world—the army of France—
and attacked over a sixteen mile front in
the Valley of the Somme.

It was a critical day for the Allies; certainly it was a most critical day in the history
of the British Army. For on that day an
answer had to be given to a very big question
indeed. Hitherto we had been fighting on
the defensive—unready, uphill, against odds.
It would have been no particular discredit
to us had we failed to hold our line. But
we had held it, and more. Now, at last, we
were ready—as ready as we were ever likely
to be. We had the men, the guns, and the
munitions. We were in a position to engage
the enemy on equal, and more than equal,
terms. And the question that the British
Empire had to answer on that day, the First
of July 1916, was this, " Are these new
amateur armies of ours, raised, trained, and
equipped in less than two years, with nothing
in the way of military tradition to uphold
them — nothing but the steady courage of
their race : are they a match for, and more

than a match for, that grim, machine-made,
iron-bound host that lies waiting for them
along that line of Picardy hills? Because if
they are *not*, we cannot win this War. We
can only make a stalemate of it."

We, looking back now over a space of
twelve months, know how our boys answered
that question. In the greatest and longest
battle that the world had yet seen, that
Army of city clerks, Midland farm - lads,
Lancashire mill-hands, Scottish miners, and
Irish corner - boys, side by side with their
great-hearted brethren from Overseas, stormed
positions which had been held impregnable for
two years, captured seventy thousand prisoners, reclaimed several hundred square miles
of the sacred soil of France, and smashed
once and for all the German-fostered fable
of the invincibility of the German Army.
It was good to have lived and suffered
during those early and lean years, if only
to be present at their fulfilment.

But at this moment the battle was only
beginning, and the bulk of their astounding
achievement was still to come. Nevertheless,
in the cautious and modest estimate of their

Commander-in-Chief, they had already done something.

*After ten days and nights of continuous fighting,* said the first official report, *our troops have completed the methodical capture of the whole of the enemy's first system of defence on a front of fourteen thousand yards. This system of defence consisted of numerous and continuous lines of fire trenches, extending to depths of from two thousand to four thousand yards, and included five strongly fortified villages, numerous heavily entrenched woods, and a large number of immensely strong redoubts. The capture of each of these trenches represented an operation of some importance, and the whole of them are now in our hands.*

Quite so. One feels, somehow, that Berlin would have got more out of such a theme.

Now let us get back to our O Pip. If you peep over the shoulder of Captain Leslie, the gunner observing officer, as he directs the fire of his battery, situated some thousands of yards in rear, through the medium of map, field-glass, and telephone, you will obtain an excellent view of to-morrow's field of battle. Present in the O Pip are Colonel Kemp, Wagstaffe, Bobby Little, and Angus M'Lachlan. The latter had been included in the party because, to quote his Commanding Officer, "he would have burst into tears if he had been left out."

Overhead roared British shells of every kind and degree of unpleasantness, for the ground in front was being "prepared" for the coming assault. The undulating landscape, running up to a low ridge on the skyline four miles away, was spouting smoke in all directions—sometimes black, sometimes green, and sometimes, where bursting shell and brick-dust intermingled, blood-red. Beyond the ridge all-conquering British aeroplanes occupied the firmament, observing for "mother" and "granny," and signalling encouragement or reproof to these ponderous but sprightly relatives as their shells hit or missed the target.

"Yes, sir," replied Leslie to Colonel Kemp's question, "that is Longueval, on the slope opposite, with the road running through on the way to Flers, over the skyline. That is Delville Wood on its right. As you see, the guns are concentrating on both places. That

is Waterlot Farm, on this side of the wood
—a sugar refinery. Regular nest of machine-
guns there, I'm told."

"No doubt we shall be able to confirm the
rumour to-morrow," said Colonel Kemp drily.
"That is Bernafay Wood on our right, I
suppose?"

"Yes, sir. We hold the whole of that. The
pear-shaped wood out beyond it—it looks as
if it were joined on, but the two are quite
separate really — is Trones Wood. It has
changed hands several times. Just at present
I don't think we hold more than the near
end. Further away, half-right, you can see
Guillemont."

"In that case," remarked Wagstaffe, "our
right flank would appear to be strongly
supported by the enemy."

"Yes. We are in a sort of right-angled
salient here. We have the enemy on our
front and our right. In fact, we form the
extreme right of the attacking front. Our
left is perfectly secure, as we now hold Ma-
metz Wood and Contalmaison. There they
are." He waved his glass to the north-west.
"When the attack takes place, I understand
that our Division will go straight ahead, for

Longueval and Delville Wood, while the next
Division makes a lateral thrust out to the
right, to push the Boche out of Trones Wood
and cover our flank."

" I believe that is so," said the Colonel.
" Bobby, take a good look at the approaches
to Longueval. That is the scene of to-
morrow's constitutional."

Bobby and Angus obediently scanned the
village through their glasses. Probably they
did not learn much. One bombarded French
village is very like another bombarded French
village. A cowering assemblage of battered
little houses; a pitiful little main street, with
its eviscerated shops and *estaminets;* a shattered church - spire. Beyond that, an en-
closure of splintered stumps that was once
an orchard. Below all, cellars, reinforced
with props and sandbags, and filled with
machine-guns. *Voilà tout!*

Presently the Gunner Captain passed word
down to the telephone operator to order the
battery to cease fire.

" Knocking off?" inquired Wagstaffe.

" For the present, yes. We are only regis-
tering this morning. Not all our batteries
are going at once, either. We don't want

Brother Boche to know our strength until we
tune up for the final chorus. We calculate
that——"

"There is a comfortable sense of decency
and order about the way we fight nowadays,"
said Colonel Kemp. "It is like working out
a problem in electrical resistance by a nice
convenient algebraical formula. Very different from the state of things last year, when
we stuck it out by employing rule of thumb
and hanging on by our eyebrows."

"The only problem we can't quite formu-
late is the machine-gun," said Leslie. "The
Boche's dug-outs here are thirty feet deep.
When crumped by our artillery he withdraws
his infantry and leaves his machine-gunners
behind, safe underground. Then, when our
guns lift and the attack comes over, his
machine-gunners appear on the surface, hoist
their guns after them with a sort of tackle
arrangement, and get to work on a pre-
arranged band of fire. The infantry can't
do them in until No Man's Land is crossed,
and—well, they don't all get across, that's
all! However, I *have* heard rumours——"

"So have we all," said Colonel Kemp.

"I forgot to tell you, Colonel," interposed

Wagstaffe, "that I met young Osborne at Divisional Headquarters last night. You remember, he left us some time ago to join the Hush! Hush! Brigade."

"I remember," said the Colonel.

By this time the party, including the Gunner Captain, were filing along a communication trench, lately the property of some German gentlemen, on their way back to headquarters.

"Did he tell you anything, Wagstaffe?" continued Colonel Kemp.

"Not much. Apparently the time of the H.H.B. is not yet. But he made an appointment with me for this evening—in the gloaming, so to speak. He is sending a car. If all he says is true, the Boche Emma Gee is booked for an eye-opener in a few weeks' time."

II.

That evening a select party of sight-seers were driven to a secluded spot behind the battle line. Here they were met by Master Osborne, obviously inflated with some important matter.

"I've got leave from my C.O. to show you the sights, sir," he announced to Colonel Kemp. "If you will all stand here and watch that wood on the opposite side of this clearing, you may see something. We don't show ourselves much except in late evening, so this is our parade-hour."

The little group took up its appointed stand and waited in the gathering dusk. In the east the sky was already twinkling with intermittent Verey lights. All around the British guns were thundering forth their hymns of hate—full-throated now, for the hour for the next great assault was approaching.

Wagstaffe's thoughts went back to a certain soft September night last year, when he and Blaikie had stood on the eastern outskirts of Bethune listening to a similar overture—the prelude to the Battle of Loos. But this overture was ten times more awful, and, from a material British point of view, ten times more inspiring. It would have thrilled old Blaikie's fighting spirit, thought Wagstaffe. But Loos had taken his friend from him, and he, Wagstaffe, only was left. What did fate hold in store for him to-morrow? he

S

wondered. And Bobby? They had both escaped marvellously so far. Well, better men had gone before them. Perhaps——

Fingers of steel bit into his biceps muscle, and the excited whinny of Angus M'Lachlan besought him to look!

*Down in the forest something stirred.* But it was not the note of a bird, as the song would have us believe. From the depths of the wood opposite came a crackling, crunching sound, as of some prehistoric beast forcing its way through tropical undergrowth. And then, suddenly, out from the thinning edge there loomed a monster—a monstrosity. It did not glide, it did not walk. It wallowed. It lurched, with now and then a laborious heave of its shoulders. It fumbled its way over a low bank matted with scrub. It crossed a ditch, by the simple expedient of rolling the ditch out flat, and waddled forward. In its path stood a young tree. The monster arrived at the tree and laid its chin lovingly against the stem. The tree leaned back, crackled, and assumed a horizontal position. In the middle of the clearing, twenty yards farther on, gaped an enormous shell-crater, a present from the Kaiser. Into

this the creature plunged blindly, to emerge,
panting and puffing, on the farther side.
Then it stopped. A magic opening appeared
in its stomach, from which emerged, grinning,
a British subaltern and his grimy associates.

And that was our friends' first encounter
with a "Tank." The secret—unlike most
secrets in this publicity - ridden War—had
been faithfully kept ; so far the Hush ! Hush !
Brigade had been little more than a legend
even to the men high up. Certainly the
omniscient Hun received the surprise of his
life when, in the early mist of a September
morning some weeks later, a line of these
selfsame tanks burst for the first time upon
his incredulous vision, waddling grotesquely
up the hill to the ridge which had defied the
British infantry so long and so bloodily,—
there to squat complacently down on the top of
the enemy's machine-guns, or spout destruction
from her own up and down beautiful trenches
which had never been intended for capture.
In fact, Brother Boche was quite plaintive
about the matter. He described the employment of such engines as wicked and brutal,
and opposed to the recognised usages of warfare. When one of these low-comedy vehicles

(named the *Crême-de-Menthe*) ambled down
the main street of the hitherto impregnable
village of Flers, with hysterical British Tom-
mies slapping her on the back, he appealed to
the civilised world to step in and forbid the
combination of vulgarism and barbarity.

"Let us at least fight like gentlemen," said
the Hun, with simple dignity. "Let us stick
to legitimate military devices—the murder of
women and children, and the emission of
chlorine gas. But Tanks—no! One must
draw the line somewhere!"

But the ill-bred *Crême-de-Menthe* took no
notice. None whatever. She simply went
waddling on—towards Berlin.


"An experiment, of course," commented
Colonel Kemp, as they returned to headquarters—"a fantastic experiment. But I
wish they were ready now. I would give
something to see one of them leading the way
into action to-morrow. It might mean saving
the lives of a good many of my boys."

# CHAPTER ELEVEN.

## THE LAST SOLO.

IT was dawn on Saturday morning, and the second phase of the Battle of the Somme was more than twenty-four hours old. The programme had opened with a night attack, always the most difficult and uncertain of enterprises, especially for soldiers who were civilians less than two years ago. But no undertaking is too audacious for men in whose veins the wine of success is beginning to throb. And this undertaking, this hazardous gamble, had succeeded all along the line. During the past day and night more than three miles of the German second system of defences, from Bazentin le Petit to the edge of Delville Wood, had received their new tenants; and already long streams of not altogether reluctant Hun prisoners were being escorted to the rear by perspiring but cheerful gentlemen with fixed bayonets.

Meanwhile—in case such of the late occupants of the line as were still at large should take a fancy to revisit their previous haunts, working parties of infantry, pioneers, and sappers were toiling at full pressure to reverse the parapets, run out barbed wire, and bestow machine-guns in such a manner as to produce a continuous lattice-work of fire along the front of the captured position.

All through the night the work had continued. As a result, positions were now tolerably secure, the intrepid "Buzzers" had included the newly grafted territory in the nervous system of the British Expeditionary Force, and Battalion Headquarters and Supply Depôts had moved up to their new positions.

To Colonel Kemp and his Adjutant, Cockerell, ensconced in a dug-out thirty feet deep, furnished with a real bed, electric-light fittings, and ornaments obviously made in Germany, entered Major Wagstaffe, encrusted with mud, but as imperturbable as ever. He saluted.

"Good morning, sir. You seem to have struck a cushie little home this time."

" Yes. The Boche officer harbours no false modesty about acknowledging his desire for creature comforts. That is where he scores off people like you and me, who pretend we like sleeping in mud. Have you been round the advanced positions ? "

" Yes. There is some pretty hard fighting going on in the village itself—the Boche still holds the north-west corner—and in the wood on the right. ' A ' Company are holding a line of broken - down cottages on our right front, but they can't make any further move until they get more bombs. The Boche is occupying various buildings opposite, but in no great strength at present. However, he seems to have plenty of machine-guns."

" I have sent up more bombs," said the Colonel. " What about ' B ' Company ? "

" ' B ' have reached their objective, and consolidated. ' C ' and ' D ' are lying close up, ready to go forward in support when required. I think ' A ' could do with a little assistance."

" I don't want to send up ' C ' and ' D ',"
replied the Colonel, " until the Divisional Reserve arrives. The Brigade has just telephoned through that reinforcements are

on the way. When they get here, we can
afford to stuff in the whole battalion. Are
'A' Company capable of handling the situation
at present?"

"Yes, I think so. Little is directing his
platoons from a convenient cellar. He was in
touch with them all when I left. But it is
possible that the Boche may make a rush
when it grows a bit lighter. At present he is
too demoralised to attempt anything beyond
intermittent machine-gun fire."

Colonel Kemp turned to Cockerell.

"Get Captain Little on the telephone," he
said, "and tell him, if the enemy displays
any disposition to counter-attack, to let me
know at once." Then he turned to Wagstaffe, and asked the question which always
lurks furtively on the tongue of a commanding
officer.

"Many—casualties?"

"'A' Company have caught it rather badly crossing the open. 'B' got off lightly.
Glen is commanding them now: Waddell was
killed leading his men in the rush to the final
objective."

Colonel Kemp sighed.

"Another good boy gone—veteran, rather.

I must write to his wife. Fairly newly married, I fancy?"

"Four months," said Wagstaffe briefly.

"What was his Christian name, do you know?"

"Walter, I think, sir," said Cockerell.

Colonel Kemp, amid the stress of battle, found time to enter a note in his pocket-diary to that effect.

Meanwhile, up in the line, "A" Company were holding on grimly to what are usually described as "certain advanced elements" of the village.

Village fighting is a confused and untidy business, but it possesses certain redeeming features. The combatants are usually so inextricably mixed up that the artillery are compelled to refrain from participation. That comes later, when you have cleared the village of the enemy, and his guns are preparing the ground for the inevitable counter-attack.

So far "A" Company had done nobly. From the moment when they had lined up before Montauban in the gross darkness preceding yesterday's dawn, until the moment when Bobby Little led them in one victorious

rush into the outskirts of the village, they
had never encountered a set-back. By sunset
they had penetrated some way farther; now
creeping stealthily forward under the shelter
of a broken wall to hurl bombs into the windows of an occupied cottage; now climbing
precariously to some commanding position in
order to open fire with a Lewis gun; now
making a sudden dash across an open space.
Such work offered peculiar opportunities to
small and well-handled parties—opportunities
of which Bobby's veterans availed themselves
right readily. Angus M'Lachlan, for instance,
accompanied by a small following of seasoned
experts, had twice rounded up parties of the
enemy in cellars, and had despatched the
same back to Headquarters with his compli-
ments and a promise of more. Mucklewame
and four men had bombed their way along a
communication trench leading to one of the
side streets of the village—a likely avenue for
a counter-attack—and having reached the end
of the trench, had built up a sandbag barri-
cade, and had held the same against the
assaults of hostile bombers until a Vickers
machine-gun had arrived in charge of an en-
ergetic subaltern of that youthful but thriv-

ing organisation, the Suicide Club, or Machine-Gun Corps, and closed the street to further Teutonic traffic.

During the night there had been periods of quiescence, devoted to consolidation, and here and there to snatches of uneasy slumber. Angus M'Lachlan, fairly in his element, had trailed his enormous length in and out of the back-yards and brick-heaps of the village; visiting every point in his irregular line, testing defences; bestowing praise; and ensuring that every man had his share of food and rest. Unutterably grimy, but inexpressibly cheerful, he reported progress to Major Wagstaffe when that nocturnal rambler visited him in the small hours.

"Well, Angus, how goes it?" inquired Wagstaffe.

"We have won the match, sir," replied Angus with simple seriousness. "We are just playing the bye now!"

And with that he crawled away, with the unnecessary stealth of a small boy playing robbers, to encourage his dour paladins to further efforts.

"We shall probably be relieved this evening," he explained to them, "and we must

make everything secure. It would never do
to leave our new positions untenable by other
troops. They might not be so reliable"—
with a paternal smile—"as you! Now, our
right flank is not safe yet. We can im-
prove the position very much if we can
secure that *estaminet*, standing up like an
island among those ruined houses on our
right front. You see the sign, *Aux Bons
Fermiers*, over the door. The trouble is that
a German machine-gun is sweeping the in-
tervening space—and we cannot see the gun!
There it goes again. See the brick-dust fly!
Keep down! They are firing mainly across
our front, but a stray bullet may come this
way."

The platoon crouched low behind their
improvised rampart of brick rubble, while
machine-gun bullets swept low, with misleading *claquement*, along the space in front of
them, from some hidden position on their right.
Presently the firing stopped. Brother Boche
was merely "losing off a belt," as a pre-
cautionary measure, at commendably regular
intervals.

"I cannot locate that gun," said Angus
impatiently. "Can you, Corporal M'Snape?"

"It is not in the Estamint itself, sirr," replied M'Snape. ("Estamint" is as near as our rank and file ever get to *estaminet*.) "It seems to be mounted some place higher up the street. I doubt they cannot see us themselves—only the ground in front of us."

"If we could reach the *estaminet* itself," said Angus thoughtfully, "we could get a more extended view. Sergeant Mucklewame, select ten men, including three bombers, and follow me. I am going to find a jumping-off place. The Lewis gun too."

Presently the little party were crouching round their officer, in a sheltered position on the right of the line—which for the moment appeared to be "in the air." Except for the intermittent streams of machine-gun fire, and an occasional shrapnel-burst overhead, all was quiet. The enemy's counter-attack was not yet ready.

"Now listen carefully," said Angus, who had just finished scribbling a despatch. "First of all, you, Bogle, take this message to the telephone, and get it sent to Company Headquarters. Now you others. We will wait till that machine-gun has fired another belt. Then, the moment it has finished, while they are getting out the next belt, I will dash across to the *estaminet* over there. M'Snape, you will come with me, but no one else—yet. If the *estaminet* seems capable of being held, I will signal to you, Sergeant Mucklewame, and you will send your party across, in driblets, not forgetting the Lewis gun. By that time I may have located the German machine-gun, so we should be able to knock it out with the Lewis."

Further speech was cut short by a punctual fantasia from the gun in question. Angus and M'Snape crouched behind the shattered wall, awaiting their chance. The firing ceased.

"*Now !*" whispered Angus.

Next moment officer and corporal were flying across the open, and before the mechanical Boche gunner could jerk the new belt into position, both had found sanctuary within the open doorway of the half-ruined *estaminet*.

Nay, more than both; for as the panting pair flung themselves into shelter, a third figure, short and stout, in an ill-fitting kilt, tumbled heavily through the doorway after them. Simultaneously a stream of machine-gun bullets went storming past.

"Just in time!" observed Angus, well pleased. "Bogle, what are you doing here?"

"I was given tae unnerstand, sirr," replied Mr Bogle calmly, "when I jined the regiment, that in action an officer's servant stands by his officer."

"That is true," conceded Angus; "but you had no right to follow me against orders. Did you not hear me say that no one but Corporal M'Snape was to come?"

"No, sirr. I doubt I was away at the 'phone."

"Well, now you are here, wait inside this doorway, where you can see Sergeant Mucklewame's party, and look out for signals. M'Snape, let us find that machine-gun."

The pair made their way to the hitherto blind side of the building, and cautiously peeped through a much-perforated shutter in the living-room.

"Do you see it, sirr?" inquired M'Snape eagerly.

Angus chuckled.

"See it? Fine! It is right in the open, in the middle of the street. Look!"

He relinquished his peep-hole. The German

machine-gun was mounted in the street itself, behind an improvised barrier of bricks and sandbags. It was less than a hundred yards away, sited in a position which, though screened from the view of Angus's platoon farther down, enabled it to sweep all the ground in front of the position. This it was now doing with great intensity, for the brief public appearance of Angus and M'Snape had effectually converted intermittent into continuous fire.

"We must get the Lewis gun over at once," muttered Angus. "It can knock that breastwork to pieces."

He crossed the house again, to see if any of Mucklewame's men had arrived.

They had not. The man with the Lewis gun was lying dead half-way across the street, with his precious weapon on the ground beside him. Two other men, both wounded, were crawling back whence they came, taking what cover they could from the storm of bullets which whizzed a few inches over their flinching bodies.

Angus hastily semaphored to Mucklewame to hold his men in check for the present. Then he returned to the other side of the house.

"How many men are serving that gun?" he said to M'Snape. "Can you see?"

"Only two, sirr, I think. I cannot see them, but that wee breastwork will not cover more than a couple of men."

"Mphm," observed Angus thoughtfully. "I expect they have been left behind to hold on. Have you a bomb about you?"

The admirable M'Snape produced from his pocket a Mills grenade, and handed it to his superior.

"Just the one, sirr," he said.

"Go you," commanded Angus, his voice rising to a more than usually Highland inflection, "and semaphore to Mucklewame that when he hears the explosion of *this*"—he pulled out the safety-pin of the grenade and gripped the grenade itself in his enormous paw—"followed, probably, by the temporary cessation of the machine-gun, he is to bring his men over here in a bunch, as hard as they can pelt. Put it as briefly as you can, but make sure he understands. He has a good signaller with him. Send Bogle to report when you have finished. Now repeat what I have said to you. . . . That's right. Carry on!"

M'Snape was gone. Angus, left alone, pensively restored the safety-pin to the grenade, and laid the grenade upon the ground beside him. Then he proceeded to write a brief letter in his field message-book. This he placed in an envelope which he took from his breast pocket. The envelope was already addressed—to the *Reverend Neil M'Lachlan, The Manse,* in a very remote Highland village. (Angus had no mother.) He closed the envelope, initialled it, and buttoned it up in his breast pocket again. After that he took up his grenade and proceeded to make a further examination of the premises. Presently he found what he wanted; and by the time Bogle arrived to announce that Sergeant Mucklewame had signalled "message understood," his arrangements were complete.

"Stay by this small hole in the wall, Bogle," he said, "and the moment the Lewis gun arrives tell them to mount it here and open fire on the enemy gun."

He left the room, leaving Bogle alone, to listen to the melancholy rustle of peeling wall-paper within and the steady crackling of bullets without. But when, peering through the improvised loophole, he next caught sight of his officer, Angus had emerged from the house by the cellar window, and was creeping with infinite caution behind the shelter of what had once been the wall of the *estaminet's* back-yard (but was now an uneven bank of bricks, averaging two feet high), in the direction of the German machine-gun. The gun, oblivious of the danger now threatening its right front, continued to fire steadily and hopefully down the street.

Slowly, painfully, Angus crawled on, until he found himself within the right angle formed by the corner of the yard. He could go no further without being seen. Between him and the German gun lay the cobbled surface of the street, offering no cover whatsoever except one mighty shell-crater, situated midway between Angus and the gun, and full to the brim with rain-water.

A single peep over the wall gave him his bearings. The gun was too far away to be reached by a grenade, even when thrown by Angus M'Lachlan. Still, it would create a diversion. It was a time bomb. He would——

He stretched out his long arm to its full extent behind him, gave one mighty overarm sweep, and with all the crackling strength of his mighty sinews, hurled the grenade.

It fell into the exact centre of the flooded shell-crater.

Angus said something under his breath which would have shocked a disciple of Kultur. Fortunately the two German gunners did not hear him. But they observed the splash, fifty yards away, and it relieved them from *ennui*, for they were growing tired of firing at nothing. They had not seen the grenade thrown, and were a little puzzled as to the cause of the phenomenon.

Four seconds later their curiosity was more than satisfied. With a muffled roar the shell-hole suddenly spouted its liquid contents and other *débris* straight to the heavens, startling them considerably and entirely obscuring their vision.

A moment later, with an exultant yell, Angus M'Lachlan was upon them. He sprang into their vision out of the descending cascade—a towering, terrible, kilted figure, bareheaded and Berserk mad. He was barely forty yards away.

Initiative is not the *forte* of the Teuton.
Number One of the German gun mechanically traversed his weapon four degrees
to the right and continued to press the
thumb-piece.  Mud and splinters of brick
sprang up round Angus's feet; but still he
came on.  He was not twenty yards away
now.  The gunner, beginning to boggle between waiting and bolting, fumbled at his
elevating gear, but Angus was right on
him before his thumbs got back to work.
Then indeed the gun spoke out with
no uncertain voice, for perhaps two seconds.
After that it ceased fire altogether.

Almost simultaneously there came a triumphant roar lower down the street, as
Mucklewame and his followers dashed obliquely across into the *estaminet*.  Mucklewame himself was carrying the derelict Lewis
gun.  In the doorway stood the watchful
M'Snape.

"This way, quick!" he shouted.  "We
have the Gairman gun spotted, and the officer
is needing the Lewis!"

But M'Snape was wrong.  The Lewis was
not required.

A few moments later, in the face of brisk sniping from the houses higher up the street, James Bogle, officer's servant—a member of that despised class which, according to the *bandar log* at home, spends the whole of its time pressing its master's trousers and smoking his cigarettes somewhere back in billets— led out a stretcher party to the German gun. Number One had been killed by a shot from Angus's revolver. Number Two had adopted Hindenburg tactics, and was no more to be seen. Angus himself was lying stone-dead a yard from the muzzle of the gun which he, single-handed, had put out of action.

His men carried him back to the *Estaminet Aux Bons Fermiers*, with the German gun, which was afterwards employed to good purpose during the desperate days of attacking and counter-attacking which ensued before the village was finally secured. They laid him in the inner room, and proceeded to put the *estaminet* in a state of defence — ready to hold the same against all comers until such time as the relieving Division should take over, and they themselves be enabled, under the kindly cloak of darkness, to carry

back their beloved officer to a more worthy
resting-place.

In the left-hand breast pocket of Angus's
tunic they found his last letter to his father.
Two German machine-gun bullets had passed
through it. It was forwarded, with a cover-
ing letter, by Colonel Kemp. In the letter
Angus's commanding officer informed Neil
M'Lachlan that his son had been recommended
posthumously for the highest honour that the
King bestows upon his soldiers.

But for the moment Mucklewame's little
band had other work to occupy them. Shelling had recommenced; the enemy were
mustering in force behind the village; and
presently a series of counter-attacks were
launched. They were successfully repelled, in
the first instance, by the remainder of "A"
Company, led in person by Bobby Little, and,
when the final struggle came, by the Battalion
Reserve under Major Wagstaffe. And throughout the whole grim struggle which ensued,
the *Estaminet Aux Bons Fermiers*, tenanted
by some of our oldest friends, proved itself
the head and corner of the successful defence.

# CHAPTER TWELVE.

## RECESSIONAL.

Two steamers lie at opposite sides of the dock. One is painted a most austere and unobtrusive grey : she is obviously a vessel with no desire to advertise her presence on the high seas. In other words, a transport. The other is dazzling white, ornamented with a good deal of green, supplemented by red. She makes an attractive picture in the early morning sun. Even by night you could not miss her, for she goes about her business with her entire hull outlined in red lights, regatta fashion, with a great luminous Red Cross blazing on either counter. Not even the Commander of a U-boat could mistake her for anything but what she is—a hospital ship.

First, let us walk round to where the grey ship is discharging her cargo. The said cargo consists of about a thousand unwounded German prisoners.

With every desire to be generous to a fallen foe, it is quite impossible to describe them as a prepossessing lot. Not one man walks like a soldier; they shamble. Naturally, they are dirty and unshaven. So are the wounded men on the white ship; but their outstanding characteristic is an invincible humanity. Beneath the mud and blood they are men— white men. But this strange throng are grey —like their ship. With their shifty eyes and curiously shaped heads, they look like nothing human. They move like over-driven beasts. We realise now why it is that the German Army has to attack in mass.

They pass down the gangway, and are shepherded into fours in the dock-shed by the Embarkation Staff, with exactly the same silent briskness that characterises the R.A.M.C. over the way. Their guard, with fixed bayonets, exhibit no more or no less concern, over them than over half a dozen Monday morning malefactors paraded for Orderly Room. Presently they will move off, possibly through the streets of the town; probably they will pass by folk against whose kith and kin they have employed every dirty trick possible in warfare. But there will be no demonstration; there never has been. As a nation we possess

a certain number of faults, on which we like
to dwell. But we have one virtue at least—
we possess a certain sense of proportion; and
we are not disposed to make subordinates
suffer because we cannot, as yet, get at the
principals.

They make a good haul. Fifteen German
regiments are here represented—possibly more,
for some have torn off their shoulder-straps to
avoid identification. Some of the units are
thinly represented; others more generously.
One famous Prussian regiment appears to
have thrown its hand in to the extent of
about five hundred.

Still, as they stand there, filthy, forlorn,
and dazed, one suddenly realises the extreme
appropriateness of a certain reference in the
Litany to All Prisoners and Captives.


II.


We turn to the hospital ship.

Two great " brows," or covered gangways,
connect her with her native land. Down
these the stretchers are beginning to pass,
having been raised from below decks by cun-
ning mechanical devices which cause no jar,

and are being conveyed into the cool shade of
the dock-shed. Here they are laid in neat
rows upon the platform, ready for transfer to
the waiting hospital train. Everything is a
miracle of quietness and order. The curious
public are afar off, held aloof by dock-gates.
(They are there in force to-day, partly to cheer
the hospital trains as they pass out, partly for
reasons connected with the grey-painted ship.)
In the dock-shed organisation and method
reign supreme.

The work has been going on without inter-
mission for several days and nights; and still
the great ships come. Another is outside,
waiting for a place at the dock. A third is
half-way across the English Channel; and
there are rumours that yet another has
selected this, the busiest moment in the opening fortnight of the Somme battle, to arrive
with a miscellaneous and irrelevant cargo of
sick and wounded from the Mediterranean.
But there is no fuss. The R.A.M.C. Staff
Officers, unruffled and cheery, control everything, apparently by a crook of the finger.
The stretcher - bearers do their work with
silent aplomb.

The occupants of the stretchers possess the
almost universal feature of a six days' beard

—always excepting those who are of an age which is not troubled by such manly accretions. They lie very still—not with the stillness of exhaustion or dejection, but with the comfortable resignation of men who have made good and have suffered in the process; but who now, with their troubles well behind them, are enduring present discomfort under the sustaining prospect of clean beds, chicken diet, and ultimate tea-parties. Such as possess them are wearing Woodbine stumps upon the lower lip.

They are quite ready to compare notes. Let us approach, and listen to a heavily bandaged gentleman who—so the label attached to him informs us—is Private Blank of the Manchesters, suffering from three " G.S." machinegun bullet wounds.

"Did the Fritzes run? Yes—they run all right! The last lot saved us trouble by running towards us—with their 'ands up! But their machine-guns—they gave us fair 'Amlet till we got across No Man's Land. After that we used the baynit, and they didn't give us no more vexatiousness. Where did we go in? Oh, near Albert. Our objective was Mary's Court, or some such place." (It is evident that the Battle of the Somme is going to add some fresh household words to our War vocabulary. "Wipers" is a veteran by this time : "Plugstreet," "Booloo," and "Armintears" are old friends. We must now make room for "Monty Ban," "La Bustle," "Mucky Farm," "Lousy Wood," and "Martinpush.")

"What were your prisoners like?"

"'Alf clemmed," said the man from Manchester.

"No rations for three days," explained a Northumberland Fusilier close by. One of his arms was strapped to his side, but the other still clasped to his bosom a German helmet. A British Tommy will cheerfully shed a limb or two in the execution of his duty, but not all the might and majesty of the Royal Army Medical Corps can force him to relinquish a fairly earned "souvenir." In fact, owing to certain unworthy suspicions as to the true significance of the initials "R.A.M.C.," he has been known to refuse chloroform.

"They couldn't get nothing up to them for four days, on account of our artillery fire," he added contentedly.

"'Barrage,' my lad!" amended a rather superior person with a lance-corporal's stripe and a bandaged foot.

Indeed, all are unanimous in affirming that
our artillery preparation was a tremendous
affair. Listen to this group of officers sunning
themselves upon the upper deck. They are
"walking cases," and must remain on board,
with what patience they may, until all the
"stretcher cases" have been evacuated.

"Loos was child's-play to it," says one—a
member of a certain immortal, or at least
irrepressible Division which has taken part in
every outburst of international unpleasantness
since the Marne. "The final hour was absolute pandemonium. And when our new
trench-mortar batteries got to work too—at
sixteen to the dozen—well, it was bad enough
for *us*; but what it must have been like at
the business end of things, Lord knows! For
a few minutes I was almost a pro-Boche!"

Other items of intelligence are gleaned.
The weather was "rotten": mud-caked garments corroborate this statement. The wire,
on the whole, was well and truly cut to pieces
everywhere, though there were spots at which
the enemy contrived to repair it. Finally,
ninety per cent of the casualties during the
assault were due to machine-gun fire.

But the fact most clearly elicited by casual
conversation is this—that the more closely

you engage in a battle, the less you know about its progress. This ship is full of officers and men who were in the thick of things for perhaps forty-eight hours on end, but who are quite likely to be utterly ignorant of what was going on round the next traverse in the trench which they had occupied.

The wounded gunners are able to give them a good deal of information. One F.O.O. saw the French advance.

"It was wonderful to see them go in," he said. "Our batteries were on the extreme right of the British line, so we were actually touching the French left flank. I had met hundreds of poilus back in billets, in cafés, and the like. To look at them strolling down a village street in their baggy uniforms, with their hands in their pockets, laughing and chatting to the children, you would never have thought they were such tigers. I remember one big fellow a few weeks ago, home on leave—*permission*—who used to frisk about with a big umbrella under his arm! I suppose that was to keep the rain off his tin hat. But when they went for Maricourt the other day, there weren't many umbrellas about—only bayonets! I tell you, they were marvels!"

It would be interesting to hear the poilu on his Allies.

The first train moves off, and another takes its place. The long lines of stretchers are thinning out now. There are perhaps a hundred left. They contain men of all units—English, Scottish, and Irish. There are Gunners, Sappers, and Infantry. Here and there among them you may note blood-stained men in dirty grey uniforms—men with dull, expressionless faces and closely cropped heads. They are tended with exactly the same care as the others. Where wounded men are concerned, the British Medical Service is strictly neutral.

A wounded corporal of the R.A.M.C. turns his head and gazes thoughtfully at one of those grey men.

"You understand English, Fritz?" he inquires.

Apparently not. Fritz continues to stare woodenly at the roof of the dock-shed.

"I should like to tell 'im a story, Jock," says the Corporal to his other neighbour. "My job is on a hospital train. 'Alf a dozen 'Un aeroplanes made a raid behind our lines, and seeing a beautiful Red Cross train—it was a new London and North-Western train, chocolate and white, with red crosses as plain as could be—well, they simply couldn't resist such a target as that! One of their machines swooped low down and dropped his bombs on us. Luckily he only got the rear coach; but I happened to be in it! D'yer 'ear that, Fritz?"

"I doot he canna understand onything," remarked the Highlander. "He's fair demoralised, like the rest. D'ye ken what happened tae me? I was gaun' back wounded, with *this*"—he indicates an arm strapped close to his side—"and there was six Fritzes came crawlin' oot o' a dug-out, and gave themselves up tae me—*me*, that was gaun' back wounded, withoot so much as my jack-knife! Demorrralised—that's it!"

"Did you 'ear," inquired a Cockney who came next in the line, "that all wounded are going to 'ave a nice little gold stripe to wear—a stripe for every wound?"

There was much interest at this.

"That'll be fine," observed a man of Kent, who had been out since Mons, and been wounded three times. "Folks 'll know now that I'm not a Derby recruit."

"Where will us wear it?" inquired a gigantic Yorkshireman from the next stretcher.

U

"Wherever you was 'it, lad!" replies the Cockney humourist.

"At that rate," comes the rueful reply, "I shall 'ave to stand oop to show mine!"

### III.

But now R.A.M.C. orderlies are at hand, and the symposium comes to an end. The stretchers are conveyed one by one into the long open coaches of the train, and each patient is slipped sideways, with gentleness and despatch, into his appointed cot.

One saloon is entirely filled with officers— the severe cases in the cots, the rest sitting where they can. A newspaper is passed round. There are delighted exclamations, especially from a second lieutenant whose features appear to be held together entirely by strips of plaster. Such parts of the countenance as can be discerned are smiling broadly.

"I *knew* we were doing well," says the bandaged one, devouring the headline; "but I never knew we were doing as well as this. Official, too! Somme battle—what? Sorry!

I apologise!" as a groan ran round the saloon.

"Never mind," said an unshaven officer with a twinkling eye, and a major's tunic wrapped loosely round him; "I expect that jest will be overworked by more people than you for the next few weeks. Does anybody happen to know where this train is going to?"

"West of England, somewhere, I believe," replied a voice.

There was an indignant groan from various north-country men.

"I suppose it is quite impossible to sort us all out at a time like this," remarked a plaintive Caledonian in an upper cot; but I fail to see why the R.A.M.C. authorities should go through the mockery of *asking* every man in the train where he wants to be taken, when the train can obviously only go to one place — or perhaps two. I was asked. I said 'Edinburgh'; and the medical wallah said, 'Righto! we'll send you to Bath!'"

"I think I can explain," remarked the wounded Major. "These trains usually go to two places—one half to Bath, the other, say, to Exeter. Bath is nearer to Edinburgh than Exeter, so they send you there. It is kindly meant, but——"

"I say," croaked a voice from another cot
—its owner was a young officer who must
just have escaped being left behind at a base
hospital as too dangerously wounded to move
—"is that a newspaper down there? Would
some one have a look, and tell me if we
have got Longueval all right? Longueval?
Long—— I got pipped, and don't quite——"

The wounded Major turned his head
quickly.

"Hallo, Bobby!" he observed cheerfully.
"That you? I didn't notice you before."

Bobby Little's hot eyes turned slowly on
Wagstaffe, and he exclaimed feverishly—

"Hallo, Major! Cheeroh! Did we stick
to Longueval all right? I've been dreaming
about it a bit, and——"

"We did," replied Wagstaffe—"thanks to
'A' Company."

Bobby Little's head fell back on the pillow,
and he remarked contentedly—

"Thanks awfully. I think I can sleep a
bit now. So long! See you later!"

His eyes closed, and he sighed happily, as
the long train slid out from the platform.

# CHAPTER THIRTEEN.

"TWO OLD SOLDIERS, BROKEN IN THE WARS."

THE smoking-room of the Britannia Club used
to be exactly like the smoking-room of every
other London club—that is to say, members
lounged about in deep chairs, and talked
shop, or scandal — or slumbered.  At any
moment you might touch a convenient bell,
and a waiter would appear at your elbow, like
a jinnee from a jar, and accept an order with
silent deference.  You could do this all day,
and the jinnee never failed to hear and obey.

That was before the War.  Now, those
idyllic days are gone.  So is the waiter.  So
is the efficacy of the bell.  You may ring, but
all that will materialise is a self-righteous
little girl, in brass buttons, who will shake
her head reprovingly, and refer you to certain
passages in the Defence of the Realm Act.

Towards the hour of six-thirty, however,

something of the old spirit of Liberty asserts itself. A throng of members—chiefly elderly gentlemen in expanded uniforms—assembles in the smoking-room, occupying all the chairs, and even overflowing on to the tables and window-sills. They are not the discursive, argumentative gathering of three years ago. They sit silent, restless, glancing furtively at their wrist-watches.

The clocks of London strike half-past six. Simultaneously the door of the smoking-room is thrown open, and a buxom young woman in cap and apron bounces in. She smiles maternally upon her fainting flock, and announces—

"The half-hour's gone. Now you can *all* have a drink!"

What would have happened if the waiter of old had done this thing, it is difficult to imagine. But the elderly gentlemen greet their Hebe with a chorus of welcome, and clamour for precedence like children at a school feast. And yet trusting wives believe that in his club, at least, a man is safe!

Major Wagstaffe, D.S.O., having been absent from London upon urgent public affairs for nearly three years, was not well versed in the newest refinements of club life.

He had arrived that morning from his Convalescent Home in the West country, and had already experienced a severe reverse at the hands of the small girl with brass buttons on venturing to order a sherry and bitters at 11.45 A.M. Consequently, at the statutory hour his voice was not uplifted with the rest, and he was served last. Not least, however; for Hebe, observing his empty sleeve, poured out his soda-water with her own fair hands, and offered to light his cigarette.

This scene of dalliance was interrupted by the arrival of Captain Bobby Little. He wore the ribbon of the Military Cross and walked with a stick—a not unusual combination in these great days. Wagstaffe made room for him upon the leather sofa, and Hebe supplied his modest wants with an indulgent smile.

An autumn and a winter had passed since the attack on Longueval. From July until the December floods, the great battle had raged. The New Armies, supplied at last with abundant munitions, a seasoned Staff, and a concerted plan of action, had answered the question propounded in a previous chapter in no uncertain fashion. Through Longueval and Delville Wood, where the graves of the Highlanders and South Africans now lie

thick, through Flers and Martinpuich, through
Pozières and Courcelette, they had fought
their way, till they had reached the ridge,
with High Wood at its summit, which the
Boche, not altogether unreasonably, had regarded as impregnable. The tide had swirled
over the crest, down the reverse slope, and up
at last to the top of that blood-stained knoll
of chalk known as the Butte de Warlencourt.
There the Hun threw in his hand. With
much loud talk upon the subject of victorious
retirements and Hindenburg Lines, he withdrew himself to a region far east of Bapaume ;
with the result that now some thousand
square miles of the soil of France had been
restored once and for all to their rightful
owners.

But Bobby and Wagstaffe had not been
there. All during the autumn and winter
they had lain softly in hospital, enjoying their
first rest for two years. Wagstaffe had lost
his left arm and gained a decoration. Bobby,
in addition to his Cross, had incurred a cracked
crown and a permanently shortened leg. But
both were well content. They had done
their bit—and something over ; and they had
emerged from the din of War with their lives,
their health, and their reason. A man who

can achieve that feat in this war can count himself fortunate.

Now, passed by a Medical Board as fit for Home Service, they had said farewell to their Convalescent Home and come to London to learn what fate Olympus held in store for them.

" Where have you been all day, Bobby ? " inquired Wagstaffe, as they sat down to dinner an hour later.

" Down in Kent," replied Bobby briefly.

" Very well : I will not probe the matter. Been to the War Office ? "

" Yes ; I was there this morning. I am to be Adjutant of a Cadet school at Great Snoreham.   What sort of a job is that likely to be ? "

" On the whole," replied Wagstaffe, " a Fairy Godmother Department job.   It might have been very much worse.   You are thoroughly up to the Adjutant business, Bobby, and of course the young officers under you will be immensely impressed by your game leg and bit of ribbon.   A very sound appointment."

" What are they going to do with you ? " asked Bobby in his turn.

" I am to command our Reserve Battalion,

with acting rank of Lieutenant - Colonel.
Think of that, my lad! They have confirmed
you in your rank as Captain, I suppose?"

"Yes."

"Good! The only trouble is that you will
be stationed in the South of England and I in
the North of Scotland; so we shall not see
quite so much of one another as of late.
However, we must get together occasionally,
and split a tin of bully for old time's sake."

"Bully? By gum!" said Bobby thoughtfully, I have almost forgotten what it tastes
like. (Fried sole, please; then roast lamb.)
Eight months in hospital do wash out certain
remembrances."

"But not all," said Wagstaffe.

"No, not all. I—I wonder how our chaps
are getting on, over there?"

"The regiment?"

"Yes. It is so hard to get definite news."

"They were in the Arras show; did better
than ever; but—well, they required a big
draft afterwards."

"The third time!" sighed Bobby. "Did
any one write to you about it?"

"Yes. Who do you think?"

"Some one in the regiment?"

"Yes."

"I did not know there were any of the old lot left. Who was it?"

"Mucklewame."

"Mucklewame? You mean to say the Boche hasn't got him yet? It's like missing Rheims Cathedral."

"Yes, they got him at Arras. Mucklewame is in hospital. Fortunately his chief wound is in the head, so he's doing nicely. Here is his letter."

Bobby took the pencilled screed and read—

MAJOR WAGSTAFFE, SIR,

*I take up my pen for to inform you that I am now in hospital in Glasgow, having become a cassuality on the 18th inst.*

*I was struck on the head by the nose-cap of a German shell (now in the possession of my quidwife). Unfortunately I was wearing one of they steel helmets at the time, with the result that I sustained a serious scalp wound, also very bad concussion. I have never had a liking for they helmets anyway.*

*The old regiment did fine in the last attack. They were specially mentioned in Orders next day. The objective was reached under heavy fire and position consolidated before we were relieved next morning.*

"Good boys!" interpolated Bobby softly.

*Colonel Carmichael, late of the Second Battn., I think, is now in command. A very nice gentleman, but we have all been missing you and the Captain.*

*They tell me that I will be for home service after this. My head is doing well, but the muscules of my right leg is badly torn. I should have liked fine for to have stayed out and come home with the other boys when we are through with Berlin.*

*Having no more to say, sir, I will now draw to a close.*

JAS. MUCKLEWAME,
*C.S.M.*

After the perusal of this characteristic *Ave atque Vale!* the two friends adjourned to the balcony, overlooking the Green Park. Here they lit their cigars in reminiscent silence, while neighbouring searchlights raked the horizon for Zeppelins which no longer came. It was a moment for confidences.

"Old Mucklewame is like the rest of us," said Wagstaffe at last.

"How?"

"Wanting to go back, and all that. I do, too—just because I'm here, I suppose. A year ago, out there, my chief ambition was to get home, with a comfortable wound and a comfortable conscience."

"Same here," admitted Bobby.

"It was the same with practically every one," said Wagstaffe. "If any man asserts that he really enjoys modern warfare, after, say, six months of it, he is a liar. In the South African show I can honestly say I was perfectly happy. We were fighting in open country against an adversary who was a gentleman; and although there was plenty of risk, the chances were that one came through all right. At any rate, there was no poison gas, and one did not see a whole platoon blown to pieces, or buried alive, by a single shell. If Brother Boer took you prisoner, he did not stick you in the stomach with a saw-edged bayonet. At the worst he pinched your trousers. But Brother Boche is a different proposition. Since he butted in, War has descended in the social scale. And modern scientific developments have turned a sporting chance of being scuppered into a mathematical certainty. And yet— and yet—old Mucklewame is right. One *hates* to be out of it—especially at the finish. When the regiment comes stumping

through London on its way back to Euston
—next year, or whenever it's going to be—
with their ragged pipers leading the way,
you would like to be at the head of 'A'
Company, Bobby, and I would give something to be exercising my old function of
whipper-in. Eh, boy?"

"Never mind," said practical Bobby. "Perhaps we shall be on somebody's glittering
Staff. What I hate to feel at present is
that the other fellows out there have got
to go on sticking it, while we——"

"And, by God," exclaimed Wagstaffe,
"what stickers they are — and were! Did
you ever see anything so splendid, Bobby,
as those six-months-old soldiers of ours—in
the early days, I mean, when we held our
trenches, week by week, under continuous
bombardment, and our gunners behind could
only help us with four or five rounds a
day?"

"I never did," said Bobby truthfully.

"I admit to you," contiuued Wagstaffe,
"that when I found myself pitchforked into
K(1) at the outbreak of the War, instead
of getting back to my old line battalion, I
was a pretty sick man. I hated everybody.
I was one of the old school — or liked to

think I was — and the ways of the new
school were not my ways. I hated the new
officers. Some of them bullied the men;
some of them allowed themselves to be
bullied by N.C.O.'s. Some never gave or
returned salutes, others went about saluting
everybody. Some came into mess in fancy
dress of their own design, and elbowed
senior officers off the hearthrug. I used to
marvel at the Colonel's patience with them.
But many of them are dead now, Bobby,
and they nearly all made good. Then the
men! After ten years in the regular Army
I hated them all — the way they lounged,
the way they dressed, the way they sat, the
way they spat. I wondered how I could
ever go on living with them. And now—I
find myself wondering how I am ever going
to live without them. We shall not see
their like again. The new lot—present lot
—are splendid fellows. They are probably
better soldiers. Certainly they are more
uniformly trained. But there was a piquancy
about our old scamps in K. that was unique
—priceless—something the world will never
see again."

"I don't know," said Bobby thoughtfully.
"That Cockney regiment which lay beside us

at Albert last summer were a pretty priceless lot. Do you remember a pair of fat
fellows in their leading platoon? We called
them Fortnum and Mason!"

"I do—particularly Fortnum. Go on!"

"Well, their bit of trench was being
shelled one day, and Fortnum, who was in
number one bay with five other men, kept
shouting out to Mason, who was round a
traverse and out of sight, to inquire how he
was getting on. 'Are you all right, Bill?'
'Are you *sure* you're all right, Bill?' 'Are
you *still* all right, Bill?' and so on. At
last Bill, getting fed up with this unusual
solicitude, yelled back — 'What's all the
anxiety abaht, eh?' And Fortnum put his
head round the traverse and explained.
'We're getting up a little sweepstake in
our bay,' he said, 'abaht the first casualty,
and I've drawn you, ole son!'"

Wagstaffe chuckled.

"That must have been the regiment that
had the historic poker party," he said.

"What yarn was that?"

"I heard it from the Brigadier—four times,
to be exact. Five men off duty were sitting
in a dug-out playing poker. A gentleman
named 'Erb had just gone to the limit on

his hand, when a rifle-grenade came into
the dug-out from somewhere and did him
in.   While they were waiting for the
stretcher-bearers, one of the other players
picked up 'Erb's hand and examined it.   Then
he laid it down again, and said—'It doesn't
matter, chaps.   Poor 'Erb wouldn't a' made
it, anyway.   I 'ad four queens.'"

"Tommy had his own ideas of fun, I'll
admit," said Bobby.   "Do you remember
those first trenches of ours at Festubert?
There was a dead Frenchman buried in
the parapet.   You know how they used to
bury people in those days?"

"I did notice it.   Go on."

"Well, this poor chap's hand stuck out,
just about four feet from the floor of the
trench.   My dug-out was only a few yards
away, and I never saw a member of my
platoon go past that spot without shaking
the hand and saying, 'Good morning,
Alphonse!'   I had it built up with sandbags
ultimately, and they were quite annoyed!"

"They have some grisly notions about life
and death," agreed Wagstaffe, "but they
are extraordinarily kind to people in trouble,
such as wounded men or prisoners.   You
can't better them."

"And now there are five millions of them.
We are all in it, at last!"

"We certainly are—men and women. I'm
afraid I had hardly realised what our women
were doing for us. Being on service all the
time, one rather overlooks what is going on
at home. But stopping a bullet puts one in
the way of a good deal of inside information
on that score."

"You mean hospital work, and so on?"

"Yes. One meets a lot of wonderful people
that way! Sisters, and ward-maids, and
V.A.D.'s——"

"I love all V.A.D.'s!" said Bobby un-
expectedly.

"Why, my youthful Mormon?"

"Because they are the people who do all
the hard work and get no limelight—like—
like——"

"Like Second Lieutenants—eh!"

"Yes, that is the idea. They have a pretty
hard time, you know," continued Bobby confidentially, "and nothing heroic, either. Giving up all the fun that a girl is entitled to;
washing dishes; answering the door-bell;
running up and down stairs; eating rotten
food. That's the sort of——"

"What is her name?" inquired the accusing

voice of Major Wagstaffe. · Then, without
waiting to extort an answer from the embarrassed Bobby—

"You are quite right. This War has certainly brought out the best in our women.
The South African War brought out our
worst. My goodness, you should have seen
the Mount Nelson Hotel at Capetown in
those days! But they have been wonderful
this time—wonderful. I love them all—the
bus-conductors, the ticket-punchers, the lift-
girls—one of them nearly shot me right through
the roof of Harrod's the other day—and the
window-cleaners, and the page-girls, and the
railway portresses! I divide my elderly heart
among them. And I met a bunch of munition
girls the other day, Bobby, coming home from
work. They were all young, and most of them
were pretty. Their faces and hands were
stained a bright orange-colour with picric acid,
and will be, I suppose, until the Boche is
booted back into his sty. In other words, they
had deliberately sacrificed their good looks for
the duration of the War. That takes a bit of
doing, I know, innocent bachelor though I
am. But bless you, they weren't worrying.
They waved their orange-coloured hands to
me, and pointed to their orange - coloured

faces, and laughed. They were *proud* of
them; they were doing their bit! They
nearly made me cry, Bobby. Yes, we are all
in it now; and those of us who come out of
it are going to find this old island of ours
a wonderfully changed place to live in."

"How? Why?" inquired Bobby. Pos-
sibly he was interested in Wagstaffe's unusual
expansiveness : possibly he hoped to steer the
conversation away from the topic of V.A.D.'s
—possibly towards it. You never know.

"Well," said Wagstaffe, " we are all going
to understand one another a great deal better
after this War."

"Who? Labour and Capital, and so on ? "

" ' Labour and Capital ' is a meaningless and
misleading expression, Bobby. For instance,
our men regard people like you and me as
Capitalists; the ordinary Brigade Major regards us as Labourers, and pretty common Labourers at that. It is all a question of degree.
But what I mean is this. You can't call your
employer a tyrant and an extortioner after
he has shared his rations with you and never
spared himself over your welfare and comfort
through weary months of trench warfare;
neither, when you have experienced a work-
ing-man's courage and cheerfulness and reli-

ability in the day of battle, can you turn round and call him a loafer and an agitator in time of peace—can you? That is just what the *Bandar Log* overlook, when they jabber about the dreadful industrial upheaval that is coming with peace. Most of all have they overlooked the fact that with the coming of peace this country will be invaded by several million of the wisest men that she has ever produced — the New British Army. That Army will consist of men who have spent three years in getting rid of mutual misapprehensions and assimilating one another's point of view—men who went out to the War ignorant and intolerant and insular, and are coming back wise to all the things that really matter. They will flood this old country, and they will make short work of the agitator, and the alarmist, and the profiteer, and all the nasty creatures that merely make a noise instead of *doing* something, and who crab the work of the Army and Navy—more especially the Navy—because there isn't a circus victory of some kind in the paper every morning. Yes, Bobby, when our boys get back, and begin to ask the *Bandar Log* what they *did* in the Great War—well, it's going to be a rotten season for *Bandar Log* generally!"

There was silence again. Presently Bobby spoke—

"When our boys get back! Some of them are never coming back again, worse luck!"

"Still," said Wagstaffe, "what they did was worth doing, and what they died for was worth while. I think their one regret to-day would be that they did not live to see their own fellows taking the offensive — the line going forward on the Somme; the old tanks waddling over the Boche trenches; and the Boche prisoners throwing up their hands and yowling 'Kamerad!' And the Kut unpleasantness cleaned up, and all the kinks in the old Salient straightened out! And Wytschaete and Messines! You remember how the two ridges used to look down into our lines at Wipers and Plugstreet? And now we're on top of both of them! Some of our friends out there — the friends who are not coming back—would have liked to know about that, Bobby. I wish they could, somehow."

"Perhaps they do," said Bobby simply.

It was close on midnight. Our "two old soldiers, broken in the Wars," levered themselves stiffly to their feet, and prepared to depart.

" Heigho!" said Wagstaffe.   " It is time
for two old wrecks like us to be in bed.  That's
what we are, Bobby—wrecks, dodderers, has-
beens!  But we have had the luck to last
longer than most.  We have dodged the
missiles of the Boche to an extent which
justifies us in claiming that we have followed
the progress of this war with a rather more
than average degree of continuity.  We were
the last of the old crowd, too.  Kemp has
got his Brigade, young Cockerell has gone
to be a Staff Captain, and—you and I are
here.  Some of the others dropped out far too
soon.  Young Lochgair, old Blaikie——"

" Waddell, too," said Bobby.  " We joined
the same day."

" And Angus M'Lachlan.  I think he would
have made the finest soldier of the lot of us,"
added Wagstaffe.  " You remember his remark
to me, that we only had the bye to play now?
He was a true prophet: we are dormy, anyhow.  (Only cold feet at Home can let us down
now.)  And he only saw three months' service!
Still, he made a great exit from this world,
Bobby, and that is the only thing that matters
in these days. . . . Ha! H'm!  As our new Allies
would say, I am beginning to ' pull heart stuff'
on you.  Let us go to bed.  Sleeping here?"

"Yes, till to-morrow.    Then off on leave."

"How much have you got?"

"A month.   I say?"

"Yes?"

"Are you doing anything on the nineteenth?"

Wagstaffe regarded his young friend suspiciously.

"Is this a catch of some kind?" he inquired.

"Oh, no.  Will you be my——" Bobby turned excessively pink, and completed his request.

Wagstaffe surveyed him resignedly.

"We all come to it, I suppose," he observed. "Only some come to it sooner than others.  Are you of age, my lad?   Have your parents——"

"I'm twenty-two," said Bobby shortly.

"Will the bridesmaids be pretty?"

"They are all peaches," replied Bobby with enthusiasm; "but nothing whatever," he added, in a voice of respectful rapture, "compared with the bride!"


### THE END.

PRINTED BY WILLIAM BLACKWOOD AND SONS.